HIGH-STEPPING HORSES

HIGH-STEPPING HORSES

COMPILED BY *Frances E. Clarke*

NEW YORK 1962 *The Macmillan Company*

Second Printing 1962

The Macmillan Company, New York
Brett-Macmillan Ltd., Galt, Ontario

Printed in the United States of America

Library of Congress catalog card number: 61-14706

Dedicated to the memory of MAN O' WAR

ACKNOWLEDGMENTS

For permission to reprint copyrighted material, grateful acknowledgment is made to the following:

Angus & Robertson, Ltd., for "Flight" by James C. Bendrodt;

Mrs. George Bambridge, Macmillan & Co., Ltd., The Macmillan Company of Canada, Ltd., and Doubleday & Company, Inc., for "The Maltese Cat" from *The Day's Work* by Rudyard Kipling;

William Blackwood & Sons, Ltd., for "Equestrian Interlude" by Tursa, selected from *Blackwood's Magazine*;

Albert & Charles Boni, Inc., for "The Horseman in the Sky" by Ambrose Bierce;

Jonathan Cape, Ltd., for "The Horseman in the Sky" from *Eyes of the Panther* by Ambrose Bierce and for "The Runaway" by Robert Frost from *The Complete Poems of Robert Frost;*

The Devin-Adair Company for "The Bride of the Man-Horse" from *The Sword of Welleran and Other Tales of Enchantment* by Lord Dunsany, Copyright 1954 by Lord Dunsany, published by The Devin-Adair Company, New York;

Harcourt, Brace and Company, Inc., for permission to reprint "The Summer of the Beautiful White Horse" from *My Name Is*

Aram by William Saroyan, Copyright 1937, 1938, 1939, 1940 by William Saroyan;

Harper & Brothers for "A Genuine Mexican Plug" from *Roughing It* by Samuel L. Clemens;

Hill and Wang, Inc., for permission to reprint "Champions of the Peak" from *The Hunting Horn and Other Stories* by Paul Annixter;

Henry Holt and Company, Inc., for "The Runaway" from *You Come Too* by Robert Frost, Copyright 1923, © 1959 by Henry Holt and Company, Inc., Copyright 1951 by Robert Frost, reprinted by permission of Holt, Rinehart and Winston, Inc.;

John Johnson for "Gato Taught Me a Lesson" by A. F. Tschiffeley;

Lloyds Bank, Ltd., and Mrs. Rachel Hichens for "The Brown Mare" from *The Brown Mare and Other Studies* by Alfred Ollivant, published by George Allen & Unwin, Ltd.;

The Macmillan Company for "The Broncho That Would Not Be Broken" from *Collected Poems* by Vachel Lindsay, Copyright 1917 by The Macmillan Company, Copyright renewed 1945 by The Macmillan Company;

Harold Matson Company for "Blue Murder" by Wilbur Daniel Steele, Copyright 1925 by Wilbur Daniel Steele, reprinted by permission of Harold Matson Company;

Robert M. McBride Company for "Pegasus, the Winged Horse of the Ancients" by Marshall Reid;

John Murray (Publishers), Ltd., and Mary Yost Associates for "Silver Blaze" by Sir Arthur Conan Doyle, reprinted from *The Memoirs of Sherlock Holmes* by permission of the Trustees of the Estate of Sir Arthur Conan Doyle;

New York Herald Tribune for "Anna Dies at 39, Veteran Horse of 'Aïda'";

The New York Times for "Horse Star of 'Aïda' Gets Final Cue" and "The King Is Dead" by Arthur Daley;

Random House, Inc., for "Arabians" from *Complete Book of Horses* by Howard J. Lewis © Copyright 1958 by Maco Magazine Corporation, reprinted by permission of Random House, Inc.;

Charles Scribner's Sons for "Joker, A Horse That Lived Up to His Name" from *Horses I Have Known* by Will James, Copyright 1940 by Will James; and for "Babieca" by Fairfax Downey, reprinted with the permission of Charles Scribner's Sons and Paul R. Reynolds & Son from *Horses of Destiny* by Fairfax Downey, Copyright 1949 by Fairfax Downey and Paul Brown;

The Society of Authors and The Royal Society for the Protection of Birds for permission to reprint "Cristiano: A Horse" by W. H. Hudson;

Henry Z. Walck, Inc., for "Bucephalus, A King's Horse," from *Each in His Way* by Alice Gall and Fleming Crew, Copyright 1937 by Henry Z. Walck, Inc.;

Mrs. Anna Katherina Wyler-Salten for "Florian Performs for Franz Joseph," a chapter in *Florian, The Emperor's Stallion* by Felix Salten (originally published in German as *Florian das Pferd des Kaisers*, Albert Muller Verlag, Ruschlikon-Zurich).

CONTENTS

HIGH-STEPPING HORSES

THE HORSEMAN IN THE SKY

AMBROSE BIERCE

I

One sunny afternoon in the autumn of the year 1861 a soldier lay in a clump of laurel by the side of the road in Western Virginia. He lay at a full length upon his stomach, his feet resting upon his toes, his head upon the left forearm. His extended right hand loosely grasped his rifle. But for the somewhat methodical disposition of his limbs and a slight rhythmic movement of his cartridge-box at the back of his belt he might have been thought to be dead. He was asleep at his post of duty. But if detected he would be dead shortly afterwards, death being the just and legal penalty of his crime.

The clump of laurel in which the criminal lay was in the angle of a road which after ascending southward a steep acclivity to that point turned sharply to the west, running along the summit for perhaps one hundred yards. There it turned southward again and went zig-zagging downward through the forest. At the salient of that second angle was a large flat rock, jutting out northward, overlooking the deep valley from which the road ascended. The rock capped a high cliff; a stone dropped from its outer edge would have fallen sheer downward one thousand feet to the tops of the pines. The angle where the soldier lay was on another spur of the same cliff. Had he been awake he would have commanded a view, not only of the short arm of the road and the jutting rock, but of the entire profile of the cliff below it. It might well have made him giddy to look.

The country was wooded everywhere except at the bottom of the valley to the northward, where there was a small natural meadow, through which flowed a stream scarcely visible from the valley's rim. This open ground looked hardly larger than an ordinary dooryard, but was really several acres in extent. Its green was more vivid than that of the enclosing forest. Away beyond it rose a line of giant cliffs similar to those upon which we are supposed to stand in our survey of the savage scene, and through which the road had somehow made its climb to the summit. The configuration of the valley, indeed, was such that from this point of observation it seemed entirely shut in, and one could but have wondered how the road which found a way out of it had found a way into it, and whence came and whither went the waters of the stream that parted the meadow more than a thousand feet below.

No country is so wild and difficult but man will make it a theatre of war; concealed in the forest at the bottom of that military rat-trap, in which half a hundred men in possession of the exits might have starved an army to submission, lay five regiments of Federal infantry. They had marched all the previous day and night and were resting. At nightfall they would take to the road again, climb to the place where their unfaithful sentinel now slept, and descending the other slope of the ridge fall upon a camp of the enemy at about midnight. Their hope was to surprise it, for the road led to the rear of it. In case of failure, their position would be perilous in the extreme; and fail they surely would should accident or vigilance apprise the enemy of the movement.

II

The sleeping sentinel in the clump of laurel was a young Virginian named Carter Druse. He was the son of wealthy parents, an only child and had known such ease and cultivation and high living as wealth and taste were able to command in the mountain country of Western Virginia. His home was but a few miles from where he now lay. One morning he had risen from the breakfast-table and said, quietly but gravely: "Father, a Union regiment has arrived at Grafton. I am going to join it."

The father lifted his leonine head, looked at the son a moment in silence, and replied: "Well, go, sir and whatever may occur, do what you conceive to be your duty. Virginia, to which you are a traitor, must get on without you. Should we both live to the end of the war, we will speak further of the matter. Your mother, as the physician has informed you, is in a most critical condition; at the best she cannot be with us longer than a few weeks, but that time is precious. It would be better not to disturb her."

So Carter Druse, bowing reverently to his father, who returned the salute with a stately courtesy that masked a breaking heart, left the home of his childhood to go soldiering. By conscience and courage, by deeds of devotion and daring, he soon commended himself to his fellows and his officers; and it was to these qualities and to some knowledge of the country that he owed his selection for his present perilous duty at the extreme outpost. Nevertheless, fatigue had been stronger than resolution and he had fallen asleep. What good or bad angel came in a dream to rouse him from his state of crime, who shall say? Without a movement, without a sound, in the profound silence and the languor of the late afternoon, some invisible messenger of fate touched with unsealing finger the eyes of his consciousness—whispered into the ear of his spirit the mysterious awakening word which no human lips ever have spoken, no human memory ever has recalled. He quietly raised his forehead from his arm and looked between the masking stems of the laurels, instinctively closing his right hand about the stock of his rifle.

His first feeling was a keen artistic delight. On a colossal pedestal, the cliff—motionless at the extreme edge of the capping rock and sharply outlined against the sky—was an equestrian statue of impressive dignity. The figure of the man sat the figure of the horse, straight and soldierly, but with the repose of a Grecian god carved in the marble which limits the suggestion of activity. The grey costume harmonized with its aerial background; the metal of accoutrement and caparison was softened and subdued by the shadow; the animal's skin had no points of high light. A carbine strikingly foreshortened lay across the pommel of the saddle, kept in place by the right hand grasping it at the "grip"; the left hand, holding the bridle rein, was invisible. In silhouette against the sky the profile of the horse was cut with the sharpness of a cameo; it looked across the heights of air to the confronting cliffs beyond. The face of the rider, turned slightly away, showed only an outline of temple and beard; he was looking downward to the bottom of the valley. Magnified by its lift against the sky and by the soldier's testifying sense of the formidableness of a near enemy the group appeared of heroic, almost colossal, size.

For an instant Druse had a strange, half-defined feeling that he had slept to the end of the war and was looking upon a noble work of art reared upon that eminence to commemorate the deeds of an heroic past of which he had been an inglorious part. The feeling was dispelled by a slight movement of the group: the horse, without moving its feet, had drawn its body slightly backward from the verge; the man remained immobile as before. Broad awake and keenly alive to the significance of the situation, Druse now brought the butt of his rifle against his cheek by cautiously pushing the barrel forward through the bushes, cocked the piece, and glancing through the sights covered a vital spot of the horseman's breast. A touch upon the trigger and all would have been well with Carter Druse. At that instant the horseman turned his head and looked in the direction of his concealed foeman—seemed to look into his very face, into his eyes, into his brave compassionate heart.

Is it then so terrible to kill an enemy in war—an enemy who has surprised a secret vital to the safety of one's self and comrades —an enemy more formidable for his knowledge than all his army for its numbers? Carter Druse grew pale; he shook in every limb, turned faint, and saw the statuesque group before him as black figures, rising, falling, moving unsteadily in arcs of circles in a fiery sky. His hand fell away from his weapon, his head slowly dropped until his face rested on the leaves in which he lay. This courageous gentleman and hardy soldier was near swooning from intensity of emotion.

It was not for long; in another moment his face was raised from earth, his hands resumed their places on the rifle, his forefinger sought the trigger; mind, heart, and eyes were clear, conscience and reason sound. He could not hope to capture that enemy; to alarm him would but send him dashing to his camp with his fatal news. The duty of the soldier was plain; the man must be shot dead from ambush—without warning, without a moment's spiritual preparation, with never so much as an unspoken prayer, he must be sent to his account. But no—there is a hope; he may have discovered nothing—perhaps he is but admiring the sublimity of the landscape. If permitted, he may turn and ride carelessly away in the direction whence he came. Surely it will be possible to judge at the instant of his withdrawing whether he knows. It may well be that his fixity of attention—Druse turned his head and looked through the deeps of air downward, as from the surface to the bottom of a translucent sea. He saw creeping across the green meadow a sinuous line of figures of men and horses—some foolish commander was permitting the soldiers of his escort to water their beasts in the open, in plain view from a dozen summits!

Druse withdrew his eyes from the valley and fixed them again upon the group of man and horse in the sky, and again it was through the sights of his rifle. But this time his aim was at the horse. In his memory, as if they were a divine mandate, rang the words of his father at their parting: "Whatever may occur, do what you conceive to be your duty." He was calm now. His teeth were firmly but not rigidly closed; his nerves were as tranquil as a sleeping babe's—not a tremor affected any muscle of his body;

his breathing, until suspended in the act of taking aim, was regular and slow. Duty had conquered; the spirit had said to the body: "Peace, be still." He fired.

III

An officer of the Federal force, who in a spirit of adventure or in quest of knowledge had left the hidden bivouac in the valley, and with aimless feet had made his way to the lower edge of a small open space near the foot of the cliff, was considering what he had to gain by pushing his exploration farther. At a distance of a quarter-mile before him, but apparently at a stone's throw, rose from its fringe of pines the gigantic face of rock, towering to so great a height above him that it made him giddy to look up to where its edge cut a sharp, rugged line against the sky. It presented a clean, vertical profile against a background of blue sky, to a point half the way down, and of distant hills, hardly less blue, thence to the tops of the trees at its base. Lifting his eyes to the dizzy altitude of its summit the officer saw an astonishing sight—a man on horseback riding down into the valley through the air!

Straight upright sat the rider, in military fashion, with a firm seat in the saddle, a strong clutch upon the rein to hold his charger from too impetuous a plunge. From his bare head his long hair streamed upward, waving like a plume. His hands were concealed in the cloud of the horse's lifted mane. The animal's body was as level as if every hoof-stroke encountered the resistant earth. Its motions were those of a wild gallop, but even as the officer looked they ceased, with all the legs thrown sharply forward as in the act of alighting from a leap. But this was a flight!

Filled with amazement and terror by this apparition of a horseman in the sky—half believing himself the chosen scribe of some new Apocalypse, the officer was overcome by the intensity of his emotions; his legs failed him and he fell. Almost at the same instant he heard a crashing sound in the trees—a sound that died without an echo—and all was still.

The officer rose to his feet, trembling. The familiar sensation of an abraded shin recalled his dazed faculties. Pulling himself together he ran rapidly, obliquely, away from the cliff to a point distant from its foot; thereabout he expected to find his man; and thereabout he naturally failed. In the fleeting instant of his vision his imagination had been so wrought upon by the apparent grace and ease and intention of the marvellous performance that it did not occur to him that the line of march of aerial cavalry is directly downward, and that he could find the objects of his search at the very foot of the cliff. A half-hour later he returned to camp.

This officer was a wise man; he knew better than to tell an incredible truth. He said nothing of what he had seen. But when the commander asked him if he had learned anything of advantage to the expedition he answered:

"Yes, sir; there is no road leading down into this valley from the southward."

The commander, knowing better, smiled.

IV

After firing his shot, Private Carter Druse reloaded his rifle and resumed his watch. Ten minutes had hardly passed when a Federal sergeant crept cautiously to him on hands and knees. Druse neither turned his head nor looked at him, but lay without motion or sign of recognition.

"Did you fire?" the sergeant whispered.

"Yes."

"At what?"

"A horse. It was standing on yonder rock—pretty far out. You see it is no longer there. It went over the cliff."

The man's face was white, but he showed no other sign of emotion. Having answered, he turned away his eyes and said no more. The sergeant did not understand.

"See here, Druse," he said, after a moment's silence, "it's no use making a mystery. I order you to report. Was there anybody on the horse?"

"Yes."

"Well?"

"My father."

The sergeant rose to his feet and walked away. "Good God!" he said.

THE BRIDE OF THE MAN-HORSE

LORD DUNSANY

On the morning of his two hundred and fiftieth year Shepperalk the centaur went to the golden coffer wherein the treasure of the centaurs was and taking from it the hoarded amulet that his father Jyshak in the years of his prime had hammered from mountain gold and set with opals bartered from the gnomes, he put it upon his wrist, and said no word but walked from his mother's cavern. And he took with him too that clarion of the centaurs, that famous silver horn, that in its time had summoned to surrender seventeen cities of Man and for twenty years had brayed at star-girt walls in the Siege of Tholdenblarns, the citadel of the gods, what time the centaurs waged their fabulous war and were not broken by any force of arms, but retreated slowly in a cloud of dust before the final miracle of the gods that they brought in their desperate need from their ultimate armoury. He took it and strode away, and his mother only sighed and let him go.

She knew that to-day he would not drink at the stream coming down from the terraces of Varpa Niger, the inner land of the mountains, that to-day he would not wonder awhile at the sunset and afterwards trot back to the cavern again to sleep on rushes pulled by rivers that knew not Man. She knew that it was with him as it had been of old with his father, and with Goom the father of Jyshak and long ago with the gods. Therefore she only sighed and let him go.

But he, coming out from the cavern that was his home, went

for the first time over the little stream and going round the corner of the crags saw glittering beneath him the mundane plain. And the wind of the autumn that was gilding the world, rushing up the slopes of the mountain, beat cold on his naked flanks. He raised his head and snorted.

"I am a man-horse now," he shouted aloud; and leaping from crag to crag he galloped by valley and chasm, by torrent-bed and scar of avalanche, until he came to the wandering leagues of the plain and left behind him for ever the Athraminaurian mountains.

His goal was Zretazoola, city of Sombelenë. What legend of Sombelenë's inhuman beauty or the wonder of her mystery had ever floated over the mundane plains to the fabulous cradle of the centaurs' race, the Athraminaurian mountains, I do not know. Yet in the blood of man there is a tide, an old sea-current rather, that is somehow akin to the twilight, which brings him rumours of beauty from however far away, as driftwood is found at sea from islands not yet discovered: and this spring-tide or current that visits the blood of man comes from the fabulous quarter of his lineage, from the legendary, the old; it takes him out of the woodlands, out to the hills, he listens to an ancient song. So it may be that Shepperalk's fabulous blood stirred in those lonely mountains away at the edge of the world to rumours that only the airy twilight knew and only confided secretly to the bat, for Shepperalk was more legendary even than man. Certain it was that he headed from the first for the city of Zretazoola, where Sombelenë in her temple dwelt; though all the mundane plains, their rivers and mountains, lay between Shepperalk's home and the city he sought.

When first the feet of the centaur touched the grass of that soft alluvial earth he blew for joy upon the silver horn, he pranced and caracoled, he gambolled over the leagues; peace came to him like a maiden with a lamp, a strange and beautiful wonder, the wind laughed as it passed him. He put his head down low to the scent of the flowers, he lifted it up to be nearer the unseen stars, he revelled through kingdoms, took rivers in his stride; how shall I tell you, ye that dwell in cities, how shall I tell you what he felt as he galloped? He felt for strength like the towers of Bei-Naräna; for lightness like those gossamer palaces that the fairy-spider builds twixt heaven and sea along the coasts of Zith; for swiftness like some bird racing up from the morning to sing in some city's spires before daylight breaks, and as the sworn companion of the wind. For joy he was as a song; the lightnings of his legendary sires, the earlier gods, began to mix with his blood; his hooves thundered. He came to the cities of men and all men trembled, for they remembered the ancient mythical wars, and now dreaded new battles and feared for the race of man. Not by Clio are these wars recorded, history does not know them, but what of that? Not all of us have sat at historians' feet, but all have learned fable and myth at their mothers' knees. And there were none that did not fear strange wars, when they saw Shepperalk swerve and leap along the public ways. So he passed from city to city.

By nights he lay down unpanting in the reeds of some marsh or a forest; before dawn he rose triumphant, and hugely drank of some river in the dark and, splashing out of it, would trot to some high place to find the sunrise and send echoing eastwards the exultant greetings of his jubilant horn. And lo! the sunrise coming up from the echoes, and the plains new-lit by the day, and the leagues spinning by like water flung from a top, and that gay companion, the loudly laughing wind, and men and the fears of men and their little cities; and, after that, great rivers and waste spaces and huge new hills and then new lands beyond them and more cities of men, and always the old companion, the glorious wind. Kingdom by kingdom slipt by, and still his breath was even. "It is a golden thing to gallop on good turf in one's youth," said the young man-horse, the centaur. "Ha, Ha," said the wind of the hills, and the winds of the plain answered.

Bells pealed in frantic towers, wise men consulted parchments, astrologers sought of the portent from the stars, the aged made subtle prophecies: "Is he not swift?" said the young. "How glad he is," said children.

Night after night brought him sleep, and day after day lit his gallop, till he came to the lands of the Athalonian men, who live by the edges of the mundane plain, and from them he came to the lands of legend again, such as those in which he was cradled on the other side of the world, and which fringe the marge of the world and mix with the twilight. And there a mighty thought came into his untired heart, for he knew that he neared Zretazoola now, the city of Sombelenë.

It was late in the day when he neared it, and clouds coloured with evening rolled low on the plain before him; he galloped on into their golden mist, and when it hid from his eyes the sight of things, the dreams in his heart awoke and romantically he pondered all those rumours that used to come to him from Sombelenë because of the fellowship of fabulous things. She dwelt, said the evening secretly to the bat, in a little temple by a lone lake-shore. A grove of cypresses screened her from the city, from Zretazoola of the climbing ways. And opposite her temple stood her tomb, her sad lake-sepulchre with open door, lest her amazing beauty and the centuries of her youth should ever give rise to the heresy among men that lovely Sombelenë was immortal: for only her beauty and her lineage were divine.

Her father had been half centaur and half god, her mother was the child of a desert-lion and that sphinx that watches the pyramids, she was more mystical than Woman.

Her beauty was as a dream, was as a song; the one dream of a lifetime dreamed on enchanted dews, the one song sung to some city by a deathless bird, blown far from his native coasts by storm in Paradise. Dawn after dawn on mountains of romance, or twilight after twilight, could never equal her beauty; all the glow-worms had not the secret among them, nor all the stars of the night; poets had never sung it nor evening guessed its meaning; the morning envied it, it was hidden from lovers.

She was unwed, unwooed.

The lions came not to woo her, because they feared her strength; and the gods dared not love her, because they knew she must die.

This was what evening whispered to the bat, this was the dream in the heart of Shepperalk as he cantered blind through the mist. And suddenly there at his hooves in the dark of the plain appeared the cleft in the legendary lands, and Zretazoola sheltering in the cleft, a-glitter with the sunset.

Swiftly and craftily he bounded down by the upper end of the cleft and entering Zretazoola by the outer gate, which looks out sheer on the stars, he galloped suddenly down the narrow streets. Many that rushed out on to balconies as he went clattering by, many that put their heads from glittering windows, are told of in golden song. Shepperalk did not tarry to give greetings, or to answer challenges from martial towers; he was down through the earthward gateway like the thunderbolt of his sires, and, like Leviathan who has leapt at an eagle, he surged into the water between the temple and tomb.

He galloped with half-shut eyes up the temple steps, and only seeing dimly through his lashes, seized Sombelenë by the hair, undazzled as yet by her beauty, and so hauled her away, and leaping with her over the floorless chasm where the waters of the lake fall unremembered away into a hole in the world, took her we know not where, to be her slave for all those centuries that are allowed to his race.

Three blasts he gave as he went upon that silver horn that is the world-old treasure of the centaurs. These were his wedding bells.

ARABIANS

HOWARD J. LEWIS

"The one horse of history whose features today exhibit in every line and limb those of its ancestors a thousand years back is the Arabian horse, with iron muscles, bones of ivory density, steel hoofs, a tail that is the flag of its patrician heritage, a neck as lovely in arch as any curve that Phidias ever dreamed, refined head, gazelle-like concavity between forehead and delicate nostrils, eyes luminous with intelligence, gentleness and spirit, and, burning steadily in every fiber, the flame of vitality." So writes J. Frank Dobie.

For a millennium or two the Arabian horse has been evoking rhapsodies from horse lovers. And no wonder. This desert steed, trained to the arts of war, with its heart of fire and skin of silk, is the wonder of the horse world. Every light-horse breed from the rangy Thoroughbred to the Quarter Horse owes many of its essential qualities to the Arabian, even through the founding stallions of the Thoroughbred line of the early Spanish horses. Credit this superb strain with intelligence, stamina, hardiness and beauty.

Give some credit, too, to the leader Mohammed, for it was his word that fired the fanatical tribes of the Moslem world to a campaign of bloody conquest that swept across the face of northern Africa bringing with them an animal that was like no other on the face of the earth. It was the Arabian horse, bred to fineness with a religious dedication, a fleet, fiery animal that could seemingly— and without food or water—run forever.

According to legend, the Arabian came by its endurance as the result of an incident during one of the early campaigns of Mohammed. After leading an army of 20,000 cavalrymen across the shimmering desert for three days without water, Mohammed sighted an oasis and gave the signal to dismount and water. As the thirst-maddened mares stampeded toward the wells, a lookout sighted indications of an ambush. Immediately the trumpeter blew the call to remount—a blast to which all the mares had been trained to respond with instant obedience. But they had smelled water, and no power on earth could make them turn away. Then, suddenly, out of the pounding herd five mares fought their way free and presented themselves to their riders. Mohammed, moved by this display of integrity, took the mares for his own mounts and later bred them to great stallions to become the founders of the modern Arabian breed.

The Arabian's reputation for intelligence has inspired stories, too, but these are more convincing. Carl Raswan, a long-time student of the breed, tells of a visit to a sheikh and his Arabian stallion, Ghazal:

"The sheikh asked me to stay behind, while he approached my own horse. Suddenly the old man stumbled—purposely, of course —and threw himself full length upon the ground.

"Ghazal snorted in fright. He wheeled about and raced at full speed toward the prostrate form of his master. There he pawed the ground and neighed loudly, as if calling to him. But when the sheikh did not answer, Ghazal began to turn the man's body cautiously with one of his hoofs.

"Ghazal nipped at the Sheikh Ammer with anxious little caresses. Then the stallion tossed his head and neighed tremulously.

" 'Ghazal!' whispered the sheikh.

"At once the horse brought his muzzle close to the man's face.

" '*Naum*—sleep,' the sheikh said.

"With a little moan, Ghazal went down on his forelegs, bent

his hocks and settled slowly upon the sand, rolling over on one side and stretching his limbs.

"Then the sheikh crawled across Ghazal's withers and seated himself upon his back.

" *'Goom*—arise!' he called out.

"With no apparent strain, Ghazal lifted his body to a kneeling position, then rose from his haunches to stand firmly on his feet."

THE ARABIAN TODAY

Although Arabian blood flows in every American breed of light horse, Arabs are bred pure on only a few ranches in the United States. The breeders claim, however, that the pure Arab is unexcelled as a saddle horse. They say that the lack of one vertebra at the base of the spine—a peculiarity of Arabs and Morgans—makes him easier to ride. As further evidence, they point to his good carriage of head and neck; his deep, well-sloped shoulders; wide and deep quarters; short, strong loins; high-set tail; compactness of middle; and a superb underpinning that never appears leggy. He has big tendons and a large knee, hock and hoof. His croup is high, his ribs well sprung.

Most distinctive feature of the Arab is his face. In profile, he has a noticeably bulging forehead and a dished face swooping down to a small nose and deep, wide jaws. The protuberant eyes are set low, wide apart and near the middle of the head. From the front, his head, with its delicate muzzle and fine lips, appears wedge-shaped. He also requires less feed than most horses and can easily assimilate the rough forage that is found on the semiarid prairies. Back in the days when grueling endurance rides were held in the rainless lands of the Middle East, it was established that the Arabians produced more energy per pound of food than any other breed.

Generally, the Arabian is shown only at walk, trot and canter.

The walk has a long, free stride, with the hind foot overstepping the forefoot by 12 inches or better. The trot is somewhat uncomfortable, but no rider will ever forget the ease of the canter.

The purebred Arabian seldom exceeds 15 hands, and his weight averages between 800 and 1,000 pounds. When an Arabian stallion is mated with a mare of another small breed, however, the offspring is frequently larger than either sire or dam.

BABIECA
Steed of El Cid

FAIRFAX DOWNEY

Legend declares that Ruy Diaz de Rivár captured his steed in battle. That national hero of Spain called El Cid—Arabic for the lord —waged many wars in the last half of the eleventh century, defending his native land against the Moors who had invaded from North Africa. But a likelier tale of how he came to own the charger, which he rode all his life and whose fame is coupled with his, runs otherwise, and the horse's strange name confirms it.

In his youth, Ruy Diaz begged his godfather, a priest of Burgos, for the gift of a colt. The priest offered him his pick from a paddock full of mares with their foals. After shrewd study, the lad selected an ugly, mangy colt. His godfather smilingly chided him:

"*Babieca* (booby in the Spanish tongue), thou hast chosen ill."

Unswerving, the boy repeated the taunt. "Babieca—that will be a good name for my horse."

Surface looks had not deceived the young horseman's eyes. Under careful tending the dirty, scabrous hide became a coat of snowy white. Babieca, true to his Arab or Barb breeding, proved his fleetness and courage, as his master won his spurs and his title as El Cid in fierce combat with the Saracens. Ruy Diaz was a champion of the realm when it struck him that none less than royalty should ride so splendid a steed as his. He journeyed to the court of King Alfonso to put Babieca through his paces. In a matchless display of horsemanship and training, a rein broke but the white charger readily answered the pressure of his rider's legs. To a loyal proffer of the horse, the King replied that he would accept him in token but that El Cid must keep him to perform astride him those feats of arms which had honored Spain and all Christendom.

The paladin and Babieca did valiant service until El Cid died in the defense of Valencia, hotly besieged by a vast Moorish army. All sign of mourning was suppressed. That night the hero's embalmed body was dressed in armor, his head encased in a helmet of gilt parchment, his shield hung around his neck, his sword fastened in his hand, and his black beard bound as was his custom with a cord beneath his breastplate. Then the dead man was braced in Babieca's saddle.

With six hundred horsemen before and a like number behind Babieca and his ghostly burden, the garrison rode forth in a desperate sally and fell on the Moorish host. Babieca charged into the thick of the fray. As always the sight of the redoubtable champion on his white steed wrought havoc among the foe. Ten thousand fleeing Moors were drowned in the sea, and the rest embarked on ships.

Babieca lived two and one-half years longer, dying at the hoary age of forty. They buried him deep, as El Cid had bade. "When ye bury Babieca, dig deep, for it were a shameful thing that he, who hath trampled down so many dogs of Moors, should be eaten by curs." Two elms were planted before the gate of the Monastery of San Pedro de Carena to mark the grave.

FLORIAN PERFORMS FOR FRANZ JOSEPH

FELIX SALTEN

Seven mounted stallions entered and filed in front of the Court Box. Seven bicornes were removed from seven heads, swung to a horizontal position, and replaced.

Florian stood in the center. To his right stood three older stallions, thoroughly trained, and to his left three equally tested ones. He resembled a fiery youth among men. In a row of white steeds he stood out as the only *pure* white one. His snowy skin, unmarred by a single speck, called up memories of cloudless sunny days, of Nature's gracious gifts. His liquid dark eyes, from whose depths his very soul shone forth, sparkled with inner fire and energy and health. Ennsbauer sat in the saddle like a carved image. With his brown frock-coat, his chiseled, reddish brown features and his fixed mien, he seemed to have been poured in metal.

The Emperor had just remarked, "Ennsbauer uses no stirrups or spurs," when the sextet began to play.

The horses walked alongside the grayish-white wainscoting. Their tails were braided with gold, with gold also their waving manes. Pair by pair they were led through the steps of the High School; approached from the far side toward the middle, and went into their syncopated, cadenced stride.

The Emperor had no eyes for any but Florian. Him he watched, deeply engrossed. His connoisseur's eye tested the animal, tested the rider, and could find no flaw that might belie the unstinted praise he had heard showered on them. His right hand played with his mustache, slowly, not with the impatient flick that spelled disappointment over something.

Ennsbauer felt the Emperor's glance like a physical touch. He stiffened. He could hope for no advancement. Nor did he need to fear a fall. Now—in the saddle, under him this unexcelled stallion whose breathing he could feel between his legs and whose readiness and willingness to obey he could sense like some organic outpouring—now doubt and pessimism vanished. The calm, collected, resolute animal gave him calmness, collectedness, resolution.

At last he rode for the applause of the Emperor, of Franz Joseph himself, and by Imperial accolade for enduring fame. Now it was his turn. . . .

Away from the wall he guided Florian, into the center of the ring. An invisible sign, and Florian, as if waiting for it, fell into the Spanish step.

Gracefully and solemnly, he lifted his legs as though one with the rhythm of the music. He gave the impression of carrying his rider collectedly and slowly by his own free will and for his own enjoyment. Jealous of space, he placed one hoof directly in front of the other.

The old Archduke Rainer could not contain himself: "Never have I seen a horse *piaffe* like that!"

Ennsbauer wanted to lead Florian out of the Spanish step, to grant him a moment's respite before the next tour. But Florian insisted on prolonging it, and Ennsbauer submitted.

Florian strode as those horses strode who, centuries ago, triumphantly and conscious of the triumphant occasion, bore Caesars and conquerors into vanquished cities or in homecoming processions. The rigid curved neck, such as ancient sculptors modeled, the heavy short body that seemed to rock on the springs of his legs, the interplay of muscle and joint, together constituted a stately performance, one that amazed the more as it gradually compelled the recognition of its rising out of the will to perfect performance. Every single movement of Florian's revealed nobility, grace, significance and distinction all in one; and in each one of his poses he was ideal model for a sculptor, the composite of all the equestrian statues of history.

The music continued and Florian, chin pressed against chest, deliberately bowed his head to the left, to the right.

"Do you remember," Elizabeth whispered to her husband, "what our boy once said about Florian? He sings—only one does not hear it."

Ennsbauer also was thinking of the words of little Leopold von Neustift as he led Florian from the Spanish step directly into the *volte*. The delight with which Florian took the change, the effortless ease with which he glided into the short, sharply cadenced gallop, encouraged Ennsbauer to try the most precise and exacting form of the *volte*, the *redoppe*, and to follow that with the *pirouette*.

As though he intended to stamp a circle into the tanbark of the floor, Florian pivoted with his hindlegs fixed to the same place, giving the breath-taking impression of a horse in full gallop that could not bolt loose from the spot, nailed to the ground by a sorcerer or by inner compulsion.

And when, right afterward, with but a short gallop around, Florian rose into the *pesade*, his two forelegs high in the air and hindlegs bent low, and accomplished this difficult feat of balance twice, three times, as if it were child's play, he needed no more spurring on. Ennsbauer simply had to let him be, as he began to *courbette*, stiffly erect. His forelegs did not beat the air, now, but hung limply side by side, folded at the knee. Thus he carried his rider, hopped forward five times without stretching his hindlegs. In the eyes of the spectators Florian's execution of the *courbette* did not impress by its bravura, or by the conquest of body heaviness by careful dressure and rehearsal, but rather as an exuberant means of getting rid of a superabundance of controlled gigantic energy.

Another short canter around the ring was shortened by Florian's own impatience when he involuntarily fell into the Spanish step. He enjoyed the music, rocked with its rhythm. These men and women and their rank were nothing to him. Still, the presence of onlookers fired him from the very outset. He wanted to please, he had a sharp longing for applause, for admiration; his ambition, goaded on by the music, threw him into a state of intoxication; youth and fettle raced through his veins like a stream overflowing on a steep grade. Nothing was difficult any longer. With his rider and with all these human beings around him, he celebrated a feast. He did not feel the ground under his feet, the light burden on his back. Gliding, dancing with the melody, he could have flown had the gay strains asked for it.

On Florian's back as he hopped on his hindlegs once, twice, Ennsbauer sat stunned, amazed.

Following two successive *croupades*, a tremendous feat, Florian went into the Spanish step still again. Tense and at the same time visibly exuberant, proud and amused, his joyously shining eyes made light of his exertions. From the *ballotade* he thrust himself into the *capriole*, rose high in the air from the standing position, forelegs and hindlegs horizontal. He soared above the ground, his head high in jubilation. Conquering!

Frenetic applause burst out all over the hall, like many fans opening and shutting, like the rustle of stiff paper being torn.

Surrounded by the six other stallions Florian stepped before the Court Box, and while the riders swung their hats in unison, he bowed his proud head just once, conscious, it seemed, of the fact that the ovation was for him and giving gracious thanks in return.

Franz Joseph himself had given the signal for the applause by lightly clapping his hands together. Now he rose and turned to

Archduke Rainer, who, as the most distant claimant to the Throne, sat farthest removed from him. Rainer was the oldest among all the archdukes, older even than the seventy-six-year-old Emperor himself. "Well, did you ever see anything like it?" Franz Joseph asked.

METZENGERSTEIN

EDGAR ALLAN POE

Pesits eram vivus—moriens tua
mors ero.—Martin Luther

Horror and fatality have been stalking abroad in all ages. Why
then give a date to the story I have to tell? Let it suffice to say,
that at the period of which I speak, there existed, in the interior of
Hungary, a settled although hidden belief in the doctrines of the
Metempsychosis. Of the doctrines themselves—that is, of their
falsity, or of their probability—I say nothing. I assert, however,
that much of our incredulity (as La Bruyère says of all our unhap-
piness) *"vient de ne pouvoir être seuls."* [1]

But there were some points in the Hungarian superstition
which were fast verging to absurdity. They—the Hungarians—
differed very essentially from their Eastern authorities. For example. *"The soul,"* said the former—I give the words of an acute
and intelligent Parisian—*"ne demeure qu'une seule fois dans un
corps sensible: au reste—un cheval, un chien, un homme même,
n'est que la ressemblance peu tangible de ces animaux."*

The families of Berlifitzing and Metzengerstein had been at
variance for centuries. Never before were two houses so illustrious,
mutually embittered by hostility so deadly. The origin of this
enmity seems to be found in the words of an ancient prophecy—
"A lofty name shall have a fearful fall when, as the rider over his

---

[1] Mercier, in *"L'an deux mille quatre cents quarante,"* seriously main-
tains the doctrines of the Metempsychosis, and J. D'Israeli says that "no
system is so simple and so little repugnant to the understanding." Colonel
Ethan Allen, the "Green Mountain Boy," is also said to have been a serious
metempsychosist.

horse, the mortality of Metzengerstein shall triumph over the im-
mortality of Berlifitzing."

To be sure the words themselves had little or no meaning. But
more trivial causes have given rise—and that no long while ago—
to consequences equally eventful. Besides, the estates, which were
contiguous, had long exercised a rival influence in the affairs of a
busy government. Moreover, near neighbors are seldom friends;
and the inhabitants of the Castle Berlifitzing might look, from their
lofty buttresses, into the very windows of the Palace Metzengerstein. Least of all had the more than feudal magnificence, thus discovered, a tendency to allay the irritable feelings of the less ancient
and less wealthy Berlifitzings. What wonder, then, that the words,
however silly, of that prediction, should have succeeded in setting
and keeping at variance two families already predisposed to quar-
rel by every instigation of hereditary jealousy? The prophecy
seemed to imply—if it implied anything—a final triumph on the
part of the already more powerful house; and was of course remembered with the more bitter animosity by the weaker and less
influential.

Wilhelm, Count Berlifitzing, although loftily descended, was,
at the epoch of this narrative, an infirm and doting old man, remarkable for nothing but an inordinate and inveterate personal
antipathy to the family of his rival, and so passionate a love of
horses, and of hunting, that neither bodily infirmity, great age,
nor mental incapacity, prevented his daily participation in the
dangers of the chase.

Frederick, Baron Metzengerstein, was, on the other hand, not
yet of age. His father, the Minister G——, died young. His
mother, the Lady Mary, followed him quickly. Frederick was, at
that time, in his eighteenth year. In a city, eighteen years are no
long period; but in a wilderness—in so magnificent a wilderness as
that old principality, the pendulum vibrates with a deeper meaning.

From some peculiar circumstances attending the administra-
tion of his father, the young Baron, at the decease of the former,

entered immediately upon his vast possessions. Such estates were seldom held before by a nobleman of Hungary. His castles were without number. The chief in point of splendor and extent was the "Palace Metzengerstein." The boundary line of his dominions was never clearly defined; but his principal park embraced a circuit of fifty miles.

Upon the succession of a proprietor so young, with a character so well known, to a fortune so unparalleled, little speculation was afloat in regard to his probable course of conduct: And, indeed, for the space of three days, the behavior of the heir out-Heroded Herod, and fairly surpassed the expectations of his most enthusiastic admirers. Shameful debaucheries—flagrant treacheries—unheard-of atrocities—gave his trembling vassals quickly to understand that no servile submission on their part—no punctilios of conscience on his own—were thenceforward to prove any security against the remorseless fangs of a petty Caligula. On the night of the fourth day, the stables of the Castle Berlifitzing were discovered to be on fire; and the unanimous opinion of the neighborhood added the crime of the incendiary to the already hideous list of the Baron's misdemeanors and enormities.

But during the tumult occasioned by this occurrence, the young nobleman himself sat apparently buried in meditation, in a vast and desolate upper apartment of the family palace of Metzengerstein. The rich although faded tapestry hangings which swung gloomily upon the walls, represented the shadowy and majestic forms or a thousand illustrious ancestors. *Here*, richermined priests, and pontifical dignitaries, familiarly seated with the autocrat and the sovereign, put a veto on the wishes of a temporal king, or restrained with the fiat of papal supremacy the rebellious sceptre of the Arch-enemy. *There*, the dark, tall statures of the Princes Metzengerstein—their muscular war-coursers plunging over the carcasses of fallen foes—startled the steadiest nerves with their vigorous expression; and *here*, again, the voluptuous and swan-like figures of the dames of days gone by, floated away in the mazes of an unreal dance to the strains of imaginary melody.

But as the Baron listened, or affected to listen, to the gradually increasing uproar in the stables of Berlifitzing—or perhaps pondered upon some more novel, some more decided act of audacity— his eyes were turned unwittingly to the figure of an enormous, and unnaturally colored horse, represented in the tapestry as belonging to a Saracen ancestor of the family of his rival. The horse itself, in the foreground of the design, stood motionless and statuelike—while, farther back, its discomfited rider perished by the dagger of a Metzengerstein.

On Frederick's lips arose a fiendish expression, as he became aware of the direction which his glance had, without his consciousness, assumed. Yet he did not remove it. On the contrary, he could by no means account for the overwhelming anxiety which appeared falling like a pall upon his senses. It was with difficulty that he reconciled his dreamy and incoherent feelings with the certainty of being awake.

The longer he gazed the more absorbing became the spell— the more impossible did it appear that he could ever withdraw his glance from the fascination of that tapestry. But the tumult without becoming suddenly more violent, with a compulsory exertion he diverted his attention to the glare of ruddy light thrown full by the flaming stables upon the windows of the apartment.

The action, however, was but momentary; his gaze returned mechanically to the wall. To his extreme horror and astonishment, the head of the gigantic steed had, in the meantime, altered its position. The neck of the animal, before arched, as if in compassion, over the prostrate body of its lord, was now extended, at full length, in the direction of the Baron. The eyes, before invisible, now wore an energetic and human expression, while they gleamed with a fiery and unusual red; and the distended lips of the apparently enraged horse left in full view his sepulchral and disgusting teeth.

Stupefied with terror, the young nobleman tottered to the

door. As he threw it open, a flash of red light, streaming far into the chamber, flung his shadow with a clear outline against the quivering tapestry; and he shuddered to perceive that shadow—as he staggered awhile upon the threshold—assuming the exact position, and precisely filling up the contour, of the relentless and triumphant murderer of the Saracen Berlifitzing.

To lighten the depression of his spirits, the Baron hurried into the open air. At the principal gate of the palace he encountered three equerries. With much difficulty, and at the imminent peril of their lives, they were restraining the convulsive plunges of a gigantic and fiery-colored horse. "Whose horse? Where did you get him?" demanded the youth, in a querulous and husky tone, as he became instantly aware that the mysterious steed in the tapestried chamber was the very counterpart of the furious animal before his eyes.

"He is your own property, sire," replied one of the equerries, "at least he is claimed by no other owner. We caught him flying, all smoking and foaming with rage, from the burning stables of the Castle Berlifitzing. Supposing him to have belonged to the old Count's stud of foreign horses, we led him back as an estray. But the grooms there disclaim any title to the creature; which is strange, since he bears evident marks of having made a narrow escape from the flames."

"The letters W. V. B. are also branded very distinctly on his forehead," interrupted a second equerry: "I supposed them, of course, to be the initials of William Von Berlifitzing—but all at the castle are positive in denying any knowledge of the horse."

"Extremely singular!" said the young Baron, with a musing air, and apparently unconscious of the meaning of his words. "He is, as you say, a remarkable horse—a prodigious horse! although, as you very justly observe, of a suspicious and untractable character; let him be mine, however," he added, after a pause, "perhaps a rider like Frederick of Metzengerstein may tame even the devil from the stables of Berlifitzing."

"You are mistaken, my lord; the horse, as I think we mentioned, is *not* from the stables of the Count. If such had been the case, we know our duty better than to bring him into the presence of a noble of your family."

"True!" observed the Baron, drily; and at that instant a page of the bed-chamber came from the palace with a heightened color, and a precipitate step. He whispered into his master's ear an account of the sudden disappearance of a small portion of the tapestry, in an apartment which he designated; entering, at the same time, into particulars of a minute and circumstantial character; but from the low tone of voice in which these latter were communicated, nothing escaped to gratify the excited curiosity of the equerries.

The young Frederick, during the conference, seemed agitated by a variety of emotions. He soon, however, recovered his composure, and an expression of determined malignancy settled upon his countenance, as he gave peremptory orders that the apartment in question should be immediately locked up, and the key placed in his own possession.

"Have you heard of the unhappy death of the old hunter Berlifitzing?" said one of his vassals to the Baron, as, after the departure of the page, the huge steed which that nobleman had adopted as his own, plunged and curveted, with redoubled fury, down the long avenue which extended from the palace to the stables of Metzengerstein.

"No!" said the Baron, turning abruptly toward the speaker, "dead! say you?"

"It is indeed true, my lord; and, to the noble of your name, will be, I imagine, no unwelcome intelligence."

A rapid smile shot over the countenance of the listener. "How died he?"

"In his rash exertions to rescue a favorite portion of the hunting stud, he has himself perished miserably in the flames."

"I—n—d—e—e—d—!" ejaculated the Baron, as if slowly and deliberately impressed with the truth of some exciting idea.

"Indeed," repeated the vassal.

"Shocking!" said the youth, calmly, and turned quietly into the palace.

From this date a marked alteration took place in the outward demeanor of the dissolute young Baron Frederick Von Metzengerstein. Indeed, his behavior disappointed every expectation, and proved little in accordance with the views of many a manœuvering mamma; while his habits and manner, still less than formerly, offered any thing congenial with those of the neighboring aristocracy. He was never to be seen beyond the limits of his own domain, and, in his wide and social world, was utterly companionless—unless, indeed, that unnatural, impetuous, and fiery-colored horse, which he henceforward continually bestrode, had any mysterious right to the title of his friend.

Numerous invitations on the part of the neighborhood for a long time, however, periodically came in. "Will the Baron honor our festivals with his presence?" "Will the Baron join us in a hunting of the boar?"—"Metzengerstein does not hunt"; "Metzengerstein will not attend," were the haughty and laconic answers.

These repeated insults were not to be endured by an imperious nobility. Such invitations became less cordial—less frequent—in time they ceased altogether. The widow of the unfortunate Count Berlifitzing was even heard to express a hope "that the Baron might be at home when he did not wish to be at home, since he disdained the company of his equals; and ride when he did not wish to ride, since he preferred the society of a horse." This to be sure was a very silly explosion of hereditary pique; and merely proved how singularly unmeaning our sayings are apt to become, when we desire to be unusually energetic.

The charitable, nevertheless, attributed the alteration in the conduct of the young nobleman to the natural sorrow of a son for the untimely loss of his parents;—forgetting, however, his atrocious and reckless behavior during the short period immediately succeeding that bereavement. Some there were, indeed, who suggested a too haughty idea of self-consequence and dignity. Others again (among whom may be mentioned the family physician) did not hesitate in speaking of morbid melancholy, and hereditary ill-health; while dark hints, of a more equivocal nature, were current among the multitude.

Indeed, the Baron's perverse attachment to his lately-acquired charger—an attachment which seemed to attain new strength from every fresh example of the animal's ferocious and demon-like propensities—at length became, in the eyes of all reasonable men, a hideous and unnatural fervor. In the glare of noon—at the dead hour of night—in sickness or in health—in calm or in tempest— the young Metzengerstein seemed riveted to the saddle of that colossal horse, whose intractable audacities so well accorded with his own spirit.

There were circumstances, moreover, which, coupled with late events, gave an unearthly and portentous character to the mania of the rider, and to the capabilities of the steed. The space passed over in a single leap had been accurately measured, and was found to exceed, by an astounding difference, the wildest expectations of the most imaginative. The Baron, besides, had no particular *name* for the animal, although all the rest of his collection were distinguished by characteristic appellations. His stable, too, was appointed at a distance from the rest; and with regard to grooming and other necessary offices, none but the owner in person had ventured to officiate, or even to enter the enclosure of that horse's particular stall. It was also to be observed, that although the three grooms, who had caught the steed as he fled from the conflagration at Berlifitzing, had succeeded in arresting his course, by means of a chain-bridle and noose—yet not one of the three could with any certainty affirm that he had, during that dangerous struggle, or at any period thereafter, actually placed his hand upon the body of the beast. Instances of peculiar intelligence in the demeanor of a noble and high-spirited horse are not to be supposed capable of exciting unreasonable attention, but there were certain circumstances which intruded themselves by force upon the most skeptical and phlegmatic; and it is said there were times when the animal caused the gaping crowd who stood around to recoil in horror from the deep and impressive meaning of his terrible stamp—times when the young Metzengerstein turned pale and shrunk away from the rapid and searching expression of his human-looking eye.

Among all the retinue of the Baron, however, none were found to doubt the ardor of that extraordinary affection which existed on the part of the young nobleman for the fiery qualities of his horse; at least, none but an insignificant and misshapen little page, whose deformities were in everybody's way, and whose opinions were of the least possible importance. He (if his ideas are worth mentioning at all) had the effrontery to assert that his master never vaulted into the saddle without an unaccountable and almost imperceptible shudder; and that, upon his return from every long continued and habitual ride, an expression of triumphant malignity distorted every muscle in his countenance.

One tempestuous night, Metzengerstein, awaking from a heavy slumber, descended like a maniac from his chamber, and, mounting in hot haste, bounded away into the mazes of the forest. An occurrence so common attracted no particular attention, but his return was looked for with intense anxiety on the part of his domestics, when, after some hours' absence, the stupendous and magnificent battlements of the Palace Metzengerstein were discovered crackling and rocking to their very foundation, under the influence of a dense and livid mass of ungovernable fire.

As the flames, when first seen, had already made so terrible a progress that all efforts to save any portion of the building were evidently futile, the astonished neighborhood stood idly around in silent if not pathetic wonder. But a new and fearful object soon riveted the attention of the multitude, and proved how much more intense is the excitement wrought in the feelings of a crowd by the contemplation of human agony, than that brought about by the most appalling spectacles of inanimate matter.

Up the long avenue of aged oaks which led from the forest to the main entrance of the Palace Metzengerstein, a steed, bearing an unbonneted and disordered rider, was seen leaping with an impetuosity which outstripped the very Demon of the Tempest.

The career of the horseman was indisputably, on his own part, uncontrollable. The agony of his countenance, the convulsive struggle of his frame, gave evidence of superhuman exertion: but no sound, save a solitary shriek, escaped from his lacerated lips, which were bitten through and through in the intensity of terror. One instant, and the clattering of hoofs resounded sharply and shrilly above the roaring of the flames and the shrieking of the winds—another, and, clearing at a single plunge the gate-way and the moat, the steed bounded far up the tottering staircases of the palace, and, with its rider, disappeared amid the whirlwind of chaotic fire.

The fury of the tempest immediately died away, and a dead calm sullenly succeeded. A white flame still enveloped the building like a shroud, and, streaming far away into the quiet atmosphere, shot forth a glare of preternatural light; while a cloud of smoke settled heavily over the battlements in the distinct colossal figure of—*a horse.*

PEGASUS, THE WINGED HORSE OF THE ANCIENTS

MARSHALL REID

Pegasus, the winged horse, knew that nowhere in the world was the grass as tender as on the high mountain slopes where swirling clouds screened the valleys far below. No man who lived on earth had ever come so high, and Pegasus was glad of that. Whenever he came near a human being in his travels he spread his broad white wings and, swift as any swallow, soared into the sky.

It was not that Pegasus was frightened, but that he had never known the love of man—or of horse either, for there was no horse like him. He had always lived alone and he liked it best that way. He kept to himself the sweet waters of his favorite fountains and the clovered grass that grew on the mountainous preserves of the Gods. The winged horse was bound by nothing. There was no call that he must obey. He might gallop and roll in the meadow as playfully as any colt, or he might soar among the clouds, more breathtakingly beautiful than any bird.

He had sprung into life full-grown when the blood of the hideous Medusa darkened the earth—that dreadful creature whose head was covered with writhing snakes instead of hair, whose face turned anyone who looked upon it into stone. When the hero Perseus slew her, his heroic deed was commemorated by the birth of this magnificent steed which rose out of her blood.

Though he was sorry for the wingless horses which he saw

working in the fields, Pegasus was not proud. He felt the need of no other pleasures than those the earth and sky afforded. The wonder and admiration of those who saw him meant less to him than the nod of a violet nestling near Pirene, that lovely spring which he had made for the Nine Muses with a single kick of his foot. He often drank deeply of its refreshing water.

It was to Pirene that the hero Bellerophon came to look for Pegasus, and where he waited day by day, thinking he saw the winged horse in every distant fleecy cloud. He knew no man had ridden Pegasus; but he knew, too, that his life depended upon Pegasus' help. The king of the country in which he lived had sent him on the most dangerous of missions. To save his own life Bellerophon must succeed, and to succeed he must ride the winged horse.

So as he watched daily by the spring, Bellerophon hardly noticed the flowers blooming about it, or heard the ripple of its clear waters. He only walked impatiently up and down, fearful that he should wait in vain.

It so often happened that Bellerophon had mistaken a cloud for Pegasus that when the horse actually came he did not recognize it in the distance. So it happened that his back was turned when the creature he sought glided with soundless grace to the far side of the spring. Huge though Pegasus was, his hoofs touched the earth daintily and his folded wings disturbed no branching bush. Fortunately Bellerophon had brought with him an enchanted bridle which he threw over the horse's head at once. No other bridle could have held him. But as soon as he felt the bit of this bridle between his teeth Pegasus stopped struggling, and stood quietly until Bellerophon sprang upon his broad back and they both soared up into the air. Rapidly the hills and valleys of the earth below them disappeared from view.

Now the task which Bellerophon had been set was to face the most terrible of monsters, the Chimaera, which lived on the top of a mountain which only the winged horse could reach. A dreadful dragon-like creature with three heads—those of a lion, a goat and a dragon—it had been laying waste the entire countryside with its fiery breath. It devoured man and animals for miles on each of its expeditions to the lowlands. The bravest warriors had been unable to conquer it. It was this creature that Bellerophon was to attack, and with the help of Pegasus hoped to conquer.

Up and up they went, higher and higher into the sky, until at last they could see, far below them, the billowing clouds of smoke which came from the dreadful monster which they sought.

Down and down they flew then, until just below them they could see amid shooting tongues of flames a sight so horrible that Pegasus checked his swift flight. He dipped one wing in a sharp turn and neighed with such force that Bellerophon had to grasp his flowing mane to avoid falling. How could Bellerophon attack without searing his horse's wings or scorching his own body? His sword was long and broad, to be sure, but he must be close to the dragon to use it. And what part should he strike? From lion's head to dragon's tail, one end of the beast was as dangerous as the other!

Yet the dragon must be slain, and man and horse must work together to subdue him. Bellerophon stroked his horse's neck and whispered encouragement to him. Then suddenly they dove like a rocket at the raging Chimaera.

With a mighty slash of his sword Bellerophon severed the lion head as they swooped away from the scorching flames. They could see even from a distance that the goat head and the snake head breathed twice as fiercely as before.

Again they dove, but this time the Chimaera slashed so venomously with his tail that Bellerophon could only strike a long and bloody gash on the flailing body. He dared lose no time lest the creature escape to its cave and there magically heal its wounds. He urged Pegasus on again and they dove once more. This time the goat head was severed and rolled down the mountain side. A third time they darted down and this time the dragon's head, now as fierce as the two combined, fell beneath Bellerophon's sword. The Chimaera lived no longer.

Rejoicing, they flew from the horrid scene and came to rest beneath the leafy shade of a great oak by the side of a rippling brook. Here they quenched their thirst, thankful to have come through with little more than a few singed feathers and a torn mantle. Side by side they rested, gazing at each other in love and admiration.

At last Bellerophon rose and lifted the golden bridle from the steed's head.

"Alas," he said, "now you will leave me, to be as free as you were before. But surely for what you have done I owe you as much as this."

Pegasus felt the magic bit slip out from between his teeth and tossed his proud head. He felt a rush of joy at being free once more. Daintily he stepped away from Bellerophon and was about to spread his wings when he heard the deep sigh of the man with whom alone, in all the world, he had shared danger. He stood still and stared at Bellerophon. Then he walked back to where Bellerophon sat sighing and lowered his head to receive the golden bit again. Pegasus had chosen friendship. With a cry of joy Bellerophon mounted, and gaily they soared into the sky, winging their way to tell the king of the death of the Chimaera.

CRISTIANO: A HORSE

W. H. HUDSON

A gaucho of my acquaintance, when I lived on the pampas and was a very young man, owned a favourite riding-horse which he had named Cristiano. To the gaucho "Christian" is simply another word for white man: he gave it that name because one of its eyes was a pale blue-grey almost white—a colour sometimes seen in the eyes of a white man, but never an Indian. The other eye was normal, though of a much lighter brown than usual. Cristiano, however, could see equally well out of both eyes, nor was the blue eye on one side correlated with deafness, as in a white cat. His sense of hearing was quite remarkable. His colour was a fine deep fawn, with black mane and tail, and altogether he was a handsome and a good, strong, sound animal; his owner was so much attached to him that he would seldom ride any other horse, and as a rule he had him saddled every day.

Now if it had only been the blue eye I should probably have forgotten Cristiano, as I made no notes about him, but I remember him vividly to this day on account of something arresting in his psychology: he was an example of the powerful effect of the conditions he had been reared in and of the persistence of habits acquired at an early period after they have ceased to be of any significance in the creature's life. Every time I was in my gaucho friend's company, when his favourite Cristiano, along with other saddle horses, was standing at the *palenque*, or row of posts set up before the door of a native rancho for visitors to fasten their horses to, my attention would be attracted to his singular behaviour. His master always tied him to the *palenque* with a long cabresto, or lariat, to give him plenty of space to move his head and whole body about quite freely. And that was just what he was always doing. A more restless horse I had never seen. His head was always raised as high as he could raise it—like an ostrich, the gauchos would say—his gaze fixed excitedly on some far object; then presently he would wheel round and stare in another direction, pointing his ears forward to listen intently to some faint far sound, which had touched his sense. The sounds that excited him most were as a rule the alarm cries of lapwings, and the objects he gazed fixedly at with a great show of apprehension would usually turn out to be a horseman on the horizon; but the sounds and sights would for some time be inaudible and invisible to us on account of their distance. Occasionally, when the bird's alarm cries grew loud and the distant rider was found to be approaching, his excitement would increase until it would discharge itself in a resounding snort—the warning or alarm note of the wild horse.

One day I remarked to my gaucho friend that his blue-eyed Cristiano amused me more than any other horse I knew. He was just like a child, and when tired of the monotony of standing tethered to the *palenque* he would start playing sentinel. He would imagine it was war-time or that an invasion of Indians was expected, and every cry of a lapwing or other alarm-giving bird, or the sight of a horseman in the distance would cause him to give a warning. But the other horses would not join in the game; they let him keep watch and wheel about this way and that, spying or pretending to spy something, and blowing his loud trumpet, without taking any notice. They simply dozed with heads down, occasionally switching off the flies with their tails or stamping a hoof to get them off their legs, or rubbing their tongues over the bits to make a rattling sound with the little iron rollers on the bridle-bar.

He laughed and said I was mistaken, that Cristiano was not

amusing himself with a game he had invented. He was born wild and belonged to a district not many leagues away but where there was an extensive marshy area impracticable for hunting on horseback. Here a band of wild horses, a small remnant of an immense troop that had formerly existed in that part, had been able to keep their freedom down to recent years. As they were frequently hunted in dry seasons when the ground was not so bad, they had become exceedingly alert and cunning, and the sight of men on horseback would send them flying to the most inaccessible places in the marshes, where it was impossible to follow them. Eventually plans were laid and the troop driven from their stronghold out into the open country, where the ground was firm, and most of them were captured. Cristiano was one of them, a colt about four or five months old, and my friend took possession of him, attracted by his blue eye and fine fawn colour. In quite a short time the colt became perfectly tame, and when broken turned out an exceptionally good riding-horse. But though so young when captured the wild alert habit was never dropped. He could never be still: when out grazing with the other horses or when standing tied to the *palenque* he was perpetually on the watch, and the cry of a plover, the sound of galloping hoofs, the sight of a horseman, would startle him and cause him to trumpet his alarm.

It strikes me as rather curious that in spite of Cristiano's evident agitation at certain sounds and sights, it never went to the length of a panic; he never attempted to break loose and run away. He behaved just as if the plover's cry or the sound of hoofs or the sight of mounted men had produced an illusion—that he was once more a wild hunted horse—yet he never acted as though it was an illusion. It was apparently nothing more than a memory and a habit.

SILVER BLAZE

SIR ARTHUR CONAN DOYLE

"I am afraid, Watson, that I shall have to go," said Holmes, as we sat down together to our breakfast one morning.

"Go! Where to?"

"To Dartmoor—to King's Pyland."

I was not surprised. Indeed, my only wonder was that he had not already been mixed up in this extraordinary case, which was the one topic of conversation through the length and breadth of England. For a whole day my companion had rambled about the room with his chin upon his chest and his brows knitted, charging and recharging his pipe with the strongest black tobacco, and absolutely deaf to any questions or remarks. Fresh editions of every paper had been sent up by our news agent only to be glanced over and tossed down into a corner. Yet, silent as he was, I knew perfectly well what it was over which he was brooding. There was but one problem before the public which could challenge his powers of analysis, and that was the singular disappearance of the favorite for the Wessex Cup, and the tragic murder of its trainer. When, therefore, he suddenly announced his intention of setting out for the scene of the drama, it was only what I had both expected and hoped for.

"I should be most happy to go down with you if I should not be in the way," said I.

"My dear Watson, you would confer a great favour upon me by coming. And I think that your time will not be mis-spent, for there are points about this case which promise to make it an absolutely unique one. We have, I think, just time to catch our train at Paddington, and I will go further into the matter upon our journey. You would oblige me by bringing with you your very excellent fieldglasses.

And so it happened that an hour or so later I found myself in the corner of a first-class carriage, flying along, *en route* for Exeter, while Sherlock Holmes, with his sharp, eager face framed in his ear-flapped travelling-cap, dipped rapidly into the bundle of fresh papers which he had procured at Paddington. We had left Reading far behind us before he thrust the last of them under the seat, and offered me his cigar-case.

"We are going well," said he, looking out of the window, and glancing at his watch. "Our rate at present is fifty-three and a half miles an hour."

"I have not observed the quarter-mile posts," said I.

"Nor have I. But the telegraph posts upon this line are sixty yards apart, and the calculation is a simple one. I presume that you have already looked into this matter of the murder of John Straker and the disappearance of Silver Blaze?"

"I have seen what the *Telegraph* and the *Chronicle* have to say."

"It is one of those cases where the art of the reasoner should be used rather for the sifting of details than for the acquiring of fresh evidence. The tragedy has been so uncommon, so complete, and of such personal importance to so many people that we are suffering from a plethora of surmise, conjecture, and hypothesis. The difficulty is to detach the framework of fact—of absolute, undeniable fact—from the embellishments of theorists and reporters. Then, having established ourselves upon this sound basis, it is our duty to see what inferences may be drawn, and which are the special points upon which the whole mystery turns. On Tuesday evening I received telegrams, both from Colonel Ross, the owner of the horse, and from Inspector Gregory, who is looking after the case, inviting my co-operation."

"Tuesday evening!" I exclaimed. "And this is Thursday morning. Why did you not go down yesterday?"

"Because I made a blunder, my dear Watson—which is, I am afraid, a more common occurrence than anyone would think who only knew me through your memoirs. The fact is that I could not believe it possible that the most remarkable horse in England could long remain concealed, especially in so sparsely inhabited a place as the north of Dartmoor. From hour to hour yesterday I expected to hear that he had been found, and that his abductor was the murderer of John Straker. When, however, another morning had come and I found that, beyond the arrest of young Fitzroy Simpson, nothing had been done, I felt that it was time for me to take action. Yet in some ways I feel that yesterday has not been wasted."

"You have formed a theory then?"

"At least, I have a grip of the essential facts of the case. I shall enumerate them to you, for nothing clears up a case so much as stating it to another person, and I can hardly expect your co-operation if I do not show you the position from which we start."

I lay back against the cushions, puffing at my cigar, while Holmes, leaning forward, with his long forefinger checking off the points upon the palm of his left hand, gave me a sketch of the events which had led to our journey.

"Silver Blaze," said he, "is from the Isonomy stock, and holds as brilliant a record as his famous ancestor. He is now in his fifth year, and has brought in turn each of the prizes of the turf to Colonel Ross, his fortunate owner. Up to the time of the catastrophe he was first favourite for the Wessex Cup, the betting being three to one on. He has always, however, been a prime favourite with the racing public, and has never yet disappointed them, so that even at short odds enormous sums of money have been laid upon him. It is obvious, therefore, that there were many people who had the strongest interest in preventing Silver Blaze from being there at the fall of the flag next Tuesday.

"This fact was, of course, appreciated at King's Pyland, where the Colonel's training stable is situated. Every precaution was taken to guard the favourite. The trainer, John Straker, is a retired jockey, who rode in Colonel Ross's colours before he became too heavy for the weighing-chair. He has served the Colonel for five years as jockey, and for seven as trainer, and has always shown himself to be a zealous and honest servant. Under him were three lads, for the establishment was a small one, containing only four horses in all. One of these lads sat up each night in the stable, while the others slept in the loft. All three bore excellent characters. John Straker, who is a married man, lived in a small villa about two hundred yards from the stables. He has no children, keeps one maid-servant, and is comfortably off. The country round is very lonely, but about half a mile to the north there is a small cluster of villas which have been built by a Tavistock contractor for the use of invalids and others who may wish to enjoy the pure Dartmoor air. Tavistock itself lies two miles to the west, while across the moor, almost about two miles distant, is the larger training establishment of Capleton, which belongs to Lord Backwater, and is managed by Silas Brown. In every other direction the moor is a complete wilderness, inhabited only by a few roaming gipsies. Such was the general situation last Monday night, when the catastrophe occurred.

"On that evening the horses had been exercised and watered as usual, and the stables were locked up at nine o'clock. Two of the lads walked up to the trainer's house, where they had supper in the kitchen, while the third, Ned Hunter, remained on guard. At a few minutes after nine the maid, Edith Baxter, carried down to the stables his supper, which consisted of a dish of curried mutton. She took no liquid, as there was a water-tap in the stables, and it was the rule that the lad on duty should drink nothing else. The maid carried a lantern with her, as it was very dark, and the path ran across the open moor.

"Edith Baxter was within thirty yards of the stables when a man appeared out of the darkness and called to her to stop. As he stepped into the circle of yellow light thrown by the lantern she saw that he was a person of gentlemanly bearing, dressed in a grey suit of tweed with a cloth cap. He wore gaiters, and carried a heavy stick with a knob to it. She was most impressed, however, by the extreme pallor of his face and by the nervousness of his manner. His age, she thought, would be rather over thirty than under it.

" 'Can you tell me where I am?' he asked. 'I had almost made up my mind to sleep on the moor when I saw the light of your lantern.'

" 'You are close to the King's Pyland training stables,' she said.

" 'Oh, indeed! What a stroke of luck!' he cried. 'I understand that a stable boy sleeps there alone every night. Perhaps that is his supper you are carrying to him. Now I am sure that you would not be too proud to earn the price of a new dress, would you?' He took a piece of white paper folded up out of his waistcoat pocket. 'See that the boy has this tonight, and you shall have the prettiest frock that money can buy.'

"She was frightened by the earnestness of his manner, and ran past him to the window through which she was accustomed to hand the meals. It was already open, and Hunter was seated at the small table inside. She had begun to tell him of what had happened, when the stranger came up again.

" 'Good evening,' said he, looking through the window, 'I wanted to have a word with you.' The girl has sworn that as he spoke she noticed the corner of the little paper packet protruding from his closed hand.

" 'What business have you here?' asked the lad.

" 'It's business that may put something into your pocket,' said the other. 'You've two horses in for the Wessex Cup—Silver Blaze and Bayard. Let me have the straight tip, and you won't be a loser. Is it a fact that at the weights Bayard could give the other a hundred yards in five furlongs, and that the stable have put their money on him?'

" 'So you're one of those damned touts!' cried the lad. 'I'll show you how we serve them in King's Pyland.' He sprang up and rushed across the stable to unloose the dog. The girl fled away to the house, but as she ran she looked back, and saw that the stranger was leaning through the window. A minute later, however, when Hunter rushed out with the hound he was gone, and though the lad ran all round the buildings he failed to find any trace of him."

"One moment!" I asked. "Did the stable boy, when he ran out with the dog, leave the door unlocked behind him?"

"Excellent, Watson; excellent!" murmured my companion. "The importance of the point struck me so forcibly, that I sent a special wire to Dartmoor yesterday to clear the matter up. The boy locked the door before he left it. The window, I may add, was not large enough for a man to get through.

"Hunter waited until his fellow-grooms had returned, when he sent a message up to the trainer and told him what had occurred. Straker was excited at hearing the account, although he does not seem to have quite realized its true significance. It left him, however, vaguely uneasy, and Mrs. Straker, waking at one in the morning, found that he was dressing. In reply to her inquiries, he said that he could not sleep on account of his anxiety about the horses, and he intended to walk down to the stables to see that all was well. She begged him to remain at home, as she could hear the rain pattering against the windows, but in spite of her entreaties he pulled on his large mackintosh and left the house.

"Mrs. Straker awoke at seven in the morning, to find that her husband had not yet returned. She dressed herself hastily, called the maid, and set off for the stables. The door was open; inside, huddled together upon a chair, Hunter was sunk in a state of absolute stupor, the favourite's stall was empty, and there were no signs of his trainer.

"The two lads who slept in the chaff-cutting loft above the harness-room were quickly roused. They had heard nothing during the night, for they are both sound sleepers. Hunter was obviously under the influence of some powerful drug; and, as no sense could be got out of him, he was left to sleep it off while the two lads and the two women ran out in search of the absentees. They still had hopes that the trainer had for some reason taken out the horse for early exercise, but on ascending the knoll near the house, from which all the neighbouring moors, were visible, they not only could see no signs of the favourite, but they perceived something which warned them that they were in the presence of a tragedy.

"About a quarter of a mile from the stables, John Straker's overcoat was flapping from a furze bush. Immediately beyond there was a bowl-shaped depression in the moor, and at the bottom of this was found the dead body of the unfortunate trainer. His head had been shattered by a savage blow from some heavy weapon, and he was wounded in the thigh, where there was a long, clean cut, inflicted evidently by some sharp instrument. It was clear, however, that Straker had defended himself vigorously against his assailants, for in his right hand he held a small knife, which was clotted with blood up to the handle, while in his left he grasped a red and black silk cravat, which was recognized by the maid as having been worn on the preceding evening by the stranger who had visited the stables.

"Hunter, on recovering from his stupor, was also quite positive as to the ownership of the cravat. He was equally certain that the same stranger had, while standing in the window, drugged his curried mutton, and so deprived the stables of their watchman.

"As to the missing horse, there were abundant proofs in the mud which lay at the bottom of the fatal hollow, that he had been there at the time of the struggle. But from that morning he has disappeared; and although a large reward has been offered, and all the gipsies of Dartmoor are on the alert, no news has come of him. Finally an analysis has shown that the remains of his supper, left by the stable lad, contain an appreciable quantity of powdered opium, while the people of the house partook of the same dish on the same night without any ill effect.

"Those are the main facts of the case stripped of all surmise and stated as baldly as possible. I shall now recapitulate what the police have done in the matter.

"Inspector Gregory, to whom the case has been committed, is an extremely competent officer. Were he gifted with imagination he might rise to great heights in his profession. On his arrival he promptly found and arrested the man upon whom suspicion naturally rested. There was little difficulty in finding him, for he was thoroughly well known in the neighbourhood. His name, it appears, was Fitzroy Simpson. He was a man of excellent birth and education, who had squandered a fortune upon the turf, and who lived now by doing a little quiet and genteel bookmaking in the sporting clubs of London. An examination of his betting-book shows that bets to the amount of five thousand pounds had been registered by him against the favourite.

"On being arrested he volunteered the statement that he had come down to Dartmoor in the hope of getting some information about the King's Pyland horses, and also about Desborough, the second favourite, which was in charge of Silas Brown, at the Capleton stables. He did not attempt to deny that he acted as described upon the evening before, but declared he had no sinister designs, and had simply wished to obtain first-hand information. When confronted with the cravat he turned very pale, and was utterly unable to account for its presence in the hand of the murdered man. His wet clothing showed that he had been out in the storm of the night before, and his stick, which was a Penang lawyer, weighted with lead, was just such a weapon as might, by repeated blows, have inflicted the terrible injuries to which the trainer had succumbed.

"On the other hand, there was no wound upon his person, while the state of Straker's knife would show that one, at least, of

"Undoubtedly. He has neither a knife nor any sign of a wound. The evidence against him is certainly very strong. He had a great interest in the disappearance of the favourite, he lies under the suspicion of having poisoned the stable boy, he was undoubtedly out in the storm, he was armed with a heavy stick, and his cravat was found in the dead man's hand. I really think we have enough to go before a jury."

Holmes shook his head. "A clever counsel would tear it all to rags," said he. "Why should he take the horse out of the stable? If he wished to injure it, why could he not do it there? Has a duplicate key been found in his possession? What chemist sold him the powdered opium? Above all where could he, a stranger to the district, hide a horse, and such a horse as this? What is his own explanation as to the paper which he wished the maid to give to the stable boy?"

"He says that it was a ten-pound note. One was found in his purse. But your other difficulties are not so formidable as they seem. He is not a stranger to the district. He has twice lodged at Tavistock in the summer. The opium was probably brought from London. The key, having served its purpose, would be hurled away. The horse may lie at the bottom of one of the pits or old mines upon the moor."

"What does he say about the cravat?"

"He acknowledges that it is his, and declares that he had lost it. But a new element has been introduced into the case which may account for his leading the horse from the stable."

Holmes pricked up his ear.

"We have found traces which show that a party of gipsies encamped on Monday night within a mile of the spot where the murder took place. On Tuesday they were gone. Now, presuming that there was some understanding between Simpson and these gipsies, might he not have been leading the horse to them when he was overtaken, and may they not have him now?"

"It is certainly possible."

"The moor is being scoured for these gipsies. I have also examined every stable and outhouse in Tavistock, and for a radius of ten miles."

"There is another training stable quite close, I understand?"

"Yes, and that is a factor which we must certainly not neglect. As Desborough, their horse, was second in the betting, they had an interest in the disappearance of the favourite. Silas Brown, the trainer, is known to have had large bets upon the event, and he was no friend to poor Straker. We have, however, examined the stables and there is nothing to connect him with the affair."

"And nothing to connect this man Simpson with the interests of the Capleton stable?"

"Nothing at all."

Holmes leaned back in the carriage and the conversation ceased. A few minutes later our driver pulled up at a neat little red-brick villa with overhanging eaves, which stood by the road. Some distance off, across a paddock, lay a long, grey-tiled building. In every other direction the low curves of the moor, bronze-coloured from the fading ferns, stretched away to the skyline, broken only by the steeples of Tavistock, and by a cluster of houses away to the westward, which marked the Capleton stables. We all sprang out with the exception of Holmes, who continued to lean back with his eyes fixed on the sky in front of him, entirely absorbed in his own thoughts. It was only when I touched his arm that he roused himself with a violent start and stepped out of the carriage.

"Excuse me," said he, turning to Colonel Ross, who had looked at him in some surprise. "I was day-dreaming." There was a gleam in his eyes and a suppressed excitement in his manner which convinced me, used as I was to his ways, that his hand was upon a clue, though I could not imagine where he had found it.

"Perhaps you would prefer at once to go to the scene of the crime, Mr. Holmes?" said Gregory.

"I think I should prefer to stay here a little and go into one or two questions of detail. Straker was brought back here, I presume?"

"Yes, he lies upstairs. The inquest is tomorrow."

"He had been in your service some years, Colonel Ross?"

"I have always found him an excellent servant."

"I presume that you made an inventory of what he had in his pockets at the time of his death, Inspector?"

"I have the things themselves in the sitting-room, if you would care to see them."

"I should be very glad."

We all filed into the front room, and sat round the central table, while the Inspector unlocked a square tin box and laid a small heap of things before us. There was a box of vestas, two inches of tallow candle, an A.D.P. briar-root pipe, a pouch of sealskin with half an ounce of long-cut cavendish, a silver watch with a gold chain, five sovereigns in gold, an aluminum pencil-case, a few papers, and an ivory-handled knife with a very delicate inflexible blade marked Weiss & Co., London.

"This is a very singular knife," said Holmes, lifting it up and examining it minutely. "I presume, as I see blood-stains upon it, that it is the one which was found in the dead man's grasp. Watson, this knife is surely in your line."

"It is what we call a cataract knife," said I.

"I thought so. A very delicate blade devised for very delicate work. A strange thing for a man to carry with him upon a rough expedition, especially as it would not shut in his pocket."

"The tip was guarded by a disc of cork which we found beside his body," said the Inspector. "His wife tells us that the knife had lain for some days upon the dressing-table, and that he had picked it up as he left the room. It was a poor weapon, but perhaps the best that he could lay his hand on at the moment."

"Very possible. How about these papers?"

"Three of them are receipted hay-dealers' accounts. One of them is a letter of instructions from Colonel Ross. This other is a milliner's account for thirty-seven pounds fifteen, made out by Madame Lesurier, of Bond Street, to William Darbyshire. Mrs. Straker tells us that Darbyshire was a friend of her husband's, and that occasionally his letters were addressed here."

"Madame Darbyshire had somewhat expensive tastes," remarked Holmes, glancing down the account. "Twenty-two guineas is rather heavy for a single costume. However, there appears to be nothing more to learn, and we may now go down to the scene of the crime."

As we emerged from the sitting-room, a woman who had been waiting in the passage took a step forward and laid her hand upon the Inspector's sleeve. Her face was haggard and thin and eager; stamped with the print of a recent horror.

"Have you got them? Have you found them?" she panted.

"No, Mrs. Straker; but Mr. Holmes here, has come from London to help us, and we shall do all that is possible."

"Surely I met you in Plymouth, at a garden-party, some time ago, Mrs. Straker," said Holmes.

"No, sir; you are mistaken."

"Dear me; why, I could have sworn to it. You wore a costume of dove-coloured silk with ostrich feather trimming."

"I never had such a dress, sir," answered the lady.

"Ah, that quite settles it," said Holmes; and, with an apology, he followed the Inspector outside. A short walk across the moor took us to the hollow in which the body had been found. At the brink of it was the furze bush upon which the coat had been hung.

"There was no wind that night, I understand," said Holmes.

"None; but very heavy rain."

"In that case the overcoat was not blown against the furze bush, but placed there."

"Yes, it was laid across the bush."

"You fill me with interest. I perceive that the ground has been trampled up a good deal. No doubt many feet have been there since Monday night."

"A piece of matting has been laid here at the side, and we have all stood upon that."

"Excellent."

"In this bag I have one of the boots which Straker wore, one of Fitzroy Simpson's shoes and a cast horseshoe of Silver Blaze."

"My dear Inspector, you surpass yourself!"

Holmes took the bag, and descending into the hollow, he pushed the matting into a more central position. Then stretching himself upon his face and leaning his chin upon his hands he made a careful study of the trampled mud in front of him.

"Halloa!" said he, suddenly, "what's this?"

It was a wax vesta, half burned, which was so coated with mud that it looked at first like a little chip of wood.

"I cannot think how I came to overlook it," said the Inspector, with an expression of annoyance.

"It was invisible, buried in the mud. I only saw it because I was looking for it."

"What! You expected to find it?"

"I thought it not unlikely." He took the boots from the bag and compared the impressions of each of them with marks upon the ground. Then he clambered up to the rim of the hollow and crawled about among the ferns and bushes.

"I am afraid that there are no more tracks," said the Inspector. "I have examined the ground very carefully for a hundred yards in each direction."

"Indeed!" said Holmes rising. "I should not have the impertinence to do it again after what you say. But I should like to take a little walk over the moors before it grows dark, that I may know my ground tomorrow, and I think that I shall put this horseshoe into my pocket for luck."

Colonel Ross, who had shown some signs of impatience at my

companion's quiet and systematic method of work, glanced at his watch.

"I wish you would come back with me, Inspector," said he. "There are several points on which I should like your advice, and especially as to whether we do not owe it to the public to remove our horse's name from the entries for the Cup."

"Certainly not," cried Holmes, with decision; "I should let the name stand."

The Colonel bowed. "I am very glad to have had your opinion, sir," said he. "You will find us at poor Straker's house when you have finished your walk, and we can drive together to Tavistock."

He turned back with the Inspector, while Holmes and I walked slowly across the moor. The sun was beginning to sink behind the stables of Capleton, and the long sloping plain in front of us was tinged with gold, deepening into rich, ruddy brown where the faded ferns and brambles caught the evening light. But the glories of the landscape were all wasted upon my companion, who was sunk in the deepest thought.

"It's this way, Watson," he said, at last. "We may leave the question of who killed John Straker for the instant, and confine ourselves to finding out what has become of the horse. Now, supposing that he broke away during or after the tragedy, where could he have gone to? The horse is a very gregarious creature. If left to himself his instincts would have been either to return to King's Pyland or go over to Capleton. Why should he run wild upon the moor? He would surely have been seen by now. And why should gipsies kidnap him? These people always clear out when they hear of trouble, for they do not wish to be pestered by the police. They could not hope to sell such a horse. They would run a great risk and gain nothing by taking him. Surely that is clear."

"Where is he then?"

"I have already said that he must have gone to King's Pyland or to Capleton. He is not at King's Pyland, therefore he is at

Capleton. Let us take that as a working hypothesis, and see what it leads us to. This part of the moor, as the Inspector remarked, is very hard and dry. But it falls away towards Capleton, and you can see from here that there is a long hollow over yonder, which must have been very wet on Monday night. If our supposition is correct, then the horse must have crossed that, and there is the point where we should look for his tracks."

We had been walking briskly during the conversation, and a few more minutes brought us to the hollow in question. At Holmes' request I walked down the bank to the right, and he to the left, but I had not taken fifty paces before I heard him give a shout, and saw him waving his hand to me. The track of a horse was plainly outlined in the soft earth in front of him, and the shoe which he took from his pocket exactly fitted the impression.

"See the value of imagination," said Holmes. "It is the one quality which Gregory lacks. We imagined what might have happened, acted upon the supposition, and find ourselves justified. Let us proceed."

We crossed the marshy bottom and passed over a quarter of a mile of dry, hard turf. Again the ground sloped and again we came on the tracks. Then we lost them for half a mile, but only to pick them up once more close to Capleton. It was Holmes who saw them first, and he stood pointing with a look of triumph upon his face. A man's track was visible beside the horse's.

"The horse was alone before," I cried.

"Quite so. It was alone before. Halloa! what is this?"

The double track turned sharp off and took the direction of King's Pyland. Holmes whistled, and we both followed along after it. His eyes were on the trail, but I happened to look a little to one side, and saw to my surprise the same tracks coming back again in the opposite direction.

"One for you, Watson," said Holmes, when I pointed it out; "you have saved us a long walk which would have brought us back on our own traces. Let us follow the return track."

We had not to go far. It ended at the paving of asphalt which led up to the gates of the Capleton stables. As we approached a groom ran out from them.

"We don't want any loiterers about here," said he.

"I only wish to ask a question," said Holmes, with his finger and thumb in his waistcoat pocket. "Should I be too early to see your master, Mr. Silas Brown, if I were to call at five o'clock to-morrow morning?"

"Bless you, sir, if anyone is about he will be, for he is always the first stirring. But here he is, sir, to answer your questions for himself. No, sir, no; it's as much as my place is worth to let him see me touch your money. Afterwards, if you like."

As Sherlock Holmes replaced the half-crown which he had drawn from his pocket, a fierce-looking elderly man strode out from the gate with a hunting-crop swinging in his hand.

"What's this, Dawson?" he cried. "No gossiping! Go about your business! And you—what the devil do you want here?"

"Ten minutes' talk with you, my good sir," said Holmes, in the sweetest of voices.

"I've no time to talk to every gadabout. We want no strangers here. Be off, or you may find a dog at your heels."

Holmes leaned forward and whispered something in the trainer's ear. He started violently and flushed to the temples.

"It's a lie!" he shouted. "An infernal lie!"

"Very good! Shall we argue about it here in public, or talk it over in your parlour?"

"Oh, come in if you wish to."

Holmes smiled. "I shall not keep you more than a few minutes, Watson," he said. "Now, Mr. Brown, I am quite at your disposal."

It was quite twenty minutes and the reds had all faded into greys before Holmes and the trainer reappeared. Never have I seen such a change as had been brought about in Silas Brown in that short time. His face was ashy pale, beads of perspiration shone upon his brow, and his hands shook until the hunting-crop wagged like a branch in the wind. His bullying, overbearing manner was all gone too, and he cringed along at my companion's side like a dog with its master.

"Your instructions will be done. It shall be done," said he.

"There must be no mistake," said Holmes, looking round at him. The other winced as he read the menace in his eyes.

"Oh, no, there shall be no mistake. It shall be there. Should I change it first or not?"

Holmes thought a little and then burst out laughing.

"No, don't," said he. "I shall write to you about it. No tricks now or—"

"Oh, you can trust me, you can trust me!"

"You must see to it on the day as if it were your own."

"You can rely upon me."

"Yes, I think I can. Well, you shall hear from me to-morrow." He turned upon his heel, disregarding the trembling hand which the other held out to him, and we set off for King's Pyland.

"A more perfect compound of the bully, coward and sneak than Master Silas Brown I have seldom met with," remarked Holmes, as we trudged along together.

"He has the horse, then?"

"He tried to bluster out of it, but I described to him so exactly what his actions had been upon that morning, that he is convinced that I was watching him. Of course, you observed the peculiarly square toes in the impressions, and that his own boots exactly corresponded to them. Again, of course, no subordinate would have dared to have done such a thing. I described to him how when, according to his custom, he was the first down, he perceived a strange horse wandering over the moor; how he went out to it, and his astonishment at recognizing him from the white fore-head which has given the favourite his name; that chance had put in his power the only horse which could beat the one upon which he had put his money. Then I described how his first impulse had been to lead him back to King's Pyland, and how the devil had shown him how he could hide the horse until the race was over, and how he had led it back and concealed it at Capleton. When I told him every detail he gave it up, and thought only of saving his own skin."

"But his stables had been searched."

"Oh, an old horse-faker like him has many a dodge."

"But are you not afraid to leave the horse in his power now, since he has every interest in injuring it?"

"My dear fellow, he will guard it as the apple of his eye. He knows that his only hope of mercy is to produce it safe."

"Colonel Ross did not impress me as a man who would be likely to show much mercy in any case."

"The matter does not rest with Colonel Ross. I follow my own methods, and tell as much or as little as I choose. That is the advantage of being unofficial. I don't know whether you observed it, Watson, but the Colonel's manner has been just a trifle cavalier to me. I am inclined now to have a little amusement at his expense. Say nothing to him about the horse."

"Certainly not, without your permission."

"And, of course, this is all quite a minor case compared with the question of who killed John Straker."

"And you will devote yourself to that?"

"On the contrary, we both go back to London by the night train."

I was thunderstruck by my friend's words. We had only been a few hours in Devonshire, and that he should give up an investigation which he had begun so brilliantly was quite incomprehensible to me. Not a word more could I draw from him until we were back at the trainer's house. The Colonel and the Inspector were awaiting us in the parlor.

"My friend and I return to town by the midnight express," said Holmes. "We have had a charming little breath of your Dartmoor air."

The Inspector opened his eyes, and the Colonel's lips curled in a sneer.

"So you despair of arresting the murderer of poor Straker," said he.

Holmes shrugged his shoulders. "There are certainly grave difficulties in the way," said he. "I have every hope, however, that your horse will start upon Tuesday, and I beg that you will have your jockey in readiness. Might I ask for a photograph of Mr. John Straker?"

The Inspector took one from an envelope in his pocket and handed it to him.

"My dear Gregory, you anticipate all my wants. If I might ask you to wait here for an instant, I have a question I should like to put to the maid."

"I must say that I am rather disappointed in our London consultant," said Colonel Ross, bluntly as my friend left the room. "I do not see that we are any further than when he came."

"At least, you have his assurance that your horse will run," said I.

"Yes I have his assurance," said the Colonel with a shrug of his shoulders. "I should prefer to have the horse."

I was about to make some reply in defence of my friend, when he entered the room again.

"Now, gentlemen," said he. "I am quite ready for Tavistock."

As we stepped into the carriage one of the stable lads held the door open for us. A sudden idea seemed to occur to Holmes, for he leaned forward and touched the lad upon the sleeve.

"You have a few sheep in the paddock," he said. "Who attends to them?"

"I do, sir."

"Have you noticed anything amiss with them of late?"

"Well, sir, not of much account; but three of them have gone lame, sir."

I could see that Holmes was extremely pleased, for he chuckled and rubbed his hands together.

"A long shot, Watson; a very long shot!" said he, pinching my arm. "Gregory, let me recommend to your attention this singular epidemic among the sheep. Drive on, coachman!"

Colonel Ross still wore an expression which showed the poor opinion which he had formed of my companion's ability, but I saw by the Inspector's face that his attention had been keenly aroused.

"You consider that to be important?" he asked.

"Exceedingly so."

"Is there any other point to which you would wish to draw my attention?"

"To the curious incident of the dog in the night-time."

"That was the curious incident," remarked Sherlock Holmes.

Four days later Holmes and I were in the train bound for Winchester, to see the race for the Wessex Cup. Colonel Ross met us, by appointment, outside the station, and we drove in his drag to the course beyond the town. His face was grave and his manner was cold in the extreme.

"I have seen nothing of my horse," said he.

"I suppose you would know him when you saw him?" asked Holmes.

The Colonel was very angry. "I have been on the turf for twenty years, and never was asked such a question as that before," said he. "A child would know Silver Blaze with his white forehead and his mottled off foreleg."

"How is the betting?"

"Well, that is the curious part of it. You could have got fifteen to one yesterday, but the price has become shorter, until you can hardly get three to one now."

"Hum!" said Holmes. "Somebody knows something, that is clear!"

As the drag drew up in the enclosure near the grandstand, I glanced at the card to see the entries. It ran:

Wessex Plate. 50 sovs. each, h. ft. with 1,000 sovs. added for four- and five-year olds. Second £300. Third £200. New course (one mile and five furlongs).

1. Mr. Heath Newton's The Negro (red cap, cinnamon jacket).
2. Colonel Wardlaw's Pugilist (pink cap, blue and black jacket).
3. Lord Backwater's Desborough (yellow cap and sleeves).
4. Colonel Ross's Silver Blaze (black cap, red jacket).
5. Duke of Balmoral's Iris (yellow and black stripes).
6. Lord Singleford's Rasper (purple cap, black sleeves).

"We scratched our other one and put all hopes on your word," said the Colonel. "Why what is that? Silver Blaze favourite?"

"Five to four against Silver Blaze!" roared the ring. "Five to four against Silver Blaze! Fifteen to five against Desborough! Five to four on the field!"

"There are the numbers up," I cried. "They are all six there."

"All six there! Then my horse is running," cried the Colonel, in great agitation. "But I don't see him. My colours have not passed."

"Only five have passed. This must be he."

As I spoke a powerful bay horse swept out from the weighing enclosure and cantered past us, bearing on its back the well-known black and red of the Colonel.

"That's not my horse!" cried the owner. "That beast has not a white hair upon its body. What is this that you have done, Mr. Holmes?"

"Well, well, let us see how he gets on," said my friend imperturbably. For a few minutes he gazed through my field-glasses. "Capital! An excellent start!" he cried suddenly. "There they are, coming round the curve!"

From our drag we had a superb view as they came up the straight. The six horses were so close together that a carpet could have covered them, but half-way up the yellow of the Capleton stable showed to the front. Before they reached us, however, Desborough's bolt was shot, and the Colonel's horse, coming away with a rush, passed the post a good six lengths before its rival, the Duke of Balmoral's Iris making a bad third.

"It's my race anyhow," gasped the Colonel, passing his hand over his eyes. "I confess that I can make neither head nor tail of it. Don't you think that you have kept up your mystery long enough, Mr. Holmes?"

"Certainly, Colonel. You shall know everything. Let us all go round and have a look at the horse together. Here he is," he continued, as we made our way into the weighing enclosure where only owners and their friends find admittance. "You have only to wash his face and his leg in spirits of wine and you will find that he is the same old Silver Blaze as ever."

"You take my breath away!"

"I found him in the hands of a faker, and took the liberty of running him just as he was sent over."

"My dear sir, you have done wonders. The horse looks very fit and well. It never went better in its life. I owe you a thousand apologies for having doubted your ability. You have done me a great service by recovering my horse. You would do me a greater still if you could lay your hands on the murderer of John Straker."

"I have done so," said Holmes, quietly.

"The Colonel and I stared at him in astonishment. "You got him! Where is he, then?"

"He is here."

"Here! Where?"

"In my company at the present time."

The Colonel flushed angrily. "I quite recognize that I am under obligations to you, Mr. Holmes," said he, "but I must regard what you have just said as either a very bad joke or an insult."

Sherlock Holmes laughed. "I assure you that I have not associated you with the crime, Colonel," said he; "the real murderer is standing immediately behind you!"

He stepped past and laid his hand upon the glossy neck of the thoroughbred.

"The horse!" cried both the Colonel and myself.

"Yes, the horse. And it may lessen his guilt if I say that it was done in self-defence, and that John Straker was a man who was entirely unworthy of your confidence. But there goes the bell; and as I stand to win a little on the next race, I shall defer a more lengthy explanation until a more fitting time."

We had the corner of a Pullman car to ourselves that evening as we whirled back to London, and I fancy that the journey was a short one to Colonel Ross as well as to myself, as we listened to our companion's narrative of the events which had occurred at the Dartmoor training stable upon that Monday night, and the means by which he had unravelled them.

"I confess," said he, "that any theories which I had formed from the newspaper reports were entirely erroneous. And yet there were indications there, had they not been overlaid by other details which concealed their true import. I went to Devonshire with the conviction that Fitzroy Simpson was the true culprit, although, of course, I saw that the evidence against him was by no means complete.

"It was while I was in the carriage, just as we reached the trainer's house, that the immense significance of the curried mutton occurred to me. You may remember that I was distrait, and remained sitting after you had all alighted. I was marvelling in my own mind how I could possibly have overlooked so obvious a clue."

"I confess," said the Colonel, "that even now I cannot see how it helps us."

"It was the first link in my chain of reasoning. Powdered opium is by no means tasteless. The flavor is not disagreeable, but it is perceptible. Were it mixed with any ordinary dish, the eater would undoubtedly detect it, and would probably eat no more. A curry was exactly the medium which would disguise this taste. By no possible supposition could this stranger, Fitzroy Simpson, have caused curry to be served in the trainer's family that night, and it is surely too monstrous a coincidence to suppose that he happened to come along with powdered opium upon the very night when a dish happened to be served which would disguise the flavour. That is unthinkable. Therefore Simpson becomes eliminated from the case, and our attention centers upon Straker and his wife, the only two people who could have chosen curried mutton for supper that night. The opium was added after the dish was set aside for the stable boy, for the others had the same for supper with no ill effects. Which of them, then, had access to that dish without the maid seeing them?

"Before deciding that question I had grasped the significance of the silence of the dog, for one true inference invariably suggests others. The Simpson incident had shown me that a dog was kept in the stables, and yet, though someone had been in and had fetched out a horse, he had not barked enough to arouse the two lads in the loft. Obviously the midnight visitor was someone whom the dog knew well.

"I was already convinced, or almost convinced, that John Straker went down to the stables in the dead of the night and took out Silver Blaze. For what purpose? For a dishonest one, obviously, or why should he drug his own stable boy? And yet I was at a loss to know why. There have been cases before now where trainers have made sure of great sums of money by laying against their own horses, through agents, and then prevented them from winning by fraud. Sometimes it is a pulling jockey. Sometimes it is some surer and subtler means. What was it here? I hoped that the contents of his pockets might help me to form a conclusion.

"And they did so. You cannot have forgotten the singular knife which was found in the dead man's hand, a knife which certainly no sane man would choose for a weapon. It was, as Dr. Watson told us, a form of knife which is used for the most delicate operations known in surgery. And it was to be used for a delicate operation that night. You must know, with your wide experience of turf matters, Colonel Ross, that it is possible to make a slight nick upon the tendons of a horse's ham, and to do it subcutaneously so as to leave absolutely no trace. A horse so treated would develop a slight lameness which would be put down to straining exercise, or a touch of rheumatism, but never to foul play."

"Villain! Scoundrel!" cried the Colonel.

"We have here the explanation of why John Straker wished to take the horse out on to the moor. So spirited a creature would have certainly roused the soundest of sleepers when it felt the prick of the knife. It was absolutely necessary to do it in the open air."

"I have been blind!" cried the Colonel. "Of course, that was why he needed the candle, and struck the match."

"Undoubtedly. But in examining his belongings, I was fortunate enough to discover, not only the method of the crime, but even its motives. As a man of the world, Colonel, you know that men do not carry other people's bills about in their pockets. We have most of us quite enough to do to settle our own. I at once concluded that Straker was leading a double life, and keeping a second establishment. The nature of the bill showed that there was a lady in the case, and one who had expensive tastes. Liberal as you are with your servants, one hardly expects that they can buy twenty-guinea walking dresses for their women. I questioned Mrs. Straker as to the dress without her knowing it, and having satisfied myself that it had never reached her, I made a note of the milliner's address, and felt that by calling there with Straker's photograph, I could easily dispose of the mythical Darbyshire.

"From that time on all was plain. Straker had led out the horse to a hollow where the light would be invisible. Simpson, in his flight, had dropped his cravat, and Straker had picked it up with some idea, perhaps, that he might use it in securing the horse's leg.

Once in the hollow he had got behind the horse, and had struck a light, but the creature, frightened at the sudden glare, and with the strange instinct of animals feeling that some mischief was intended, had lashed out, and the steel shoe had struck Straker full on the forehead. He had already, in spite of the rain, taken off his overcoat in order to do his delicate task, and so, as he fell, his knife gashed his thigh. Do I make it plain?"

"Wonderful!" cried the Colonel. "Wonderful! You might have been there."

"My final shot was, I confess, a very long one. It struck me that so astute a man as Straker would not undertake this delicate tendon-nicking without a little practice. What could he practise on? My eyes fell upon the sheep, and I asked a question which, rather to my surprise, showed that my surmise was correct."

"You have made it perfectly clear, Mr. Holmes."

"When I returned to London, I called upon the milliner, who at once recognized Straker as an excellent customer, of the name of Darbyshire, who had a dashing wife with a strong partiality for expensive dresses. I have no doubt that this woman had plunged over head and ears in debt, so led him into this miserable plot."

"You have explained all but one thing," cried the Colonel. "Where was the horse?"

"Ah, it bolted and was cared for by one of your neighbours. We must have an amnesty in that direction, I think. This is Clapham Junction, if I am not mistaken, and we shall be in Victoria in less than ten minutes. If you care to smoke a cigar in our rooms, Colonel, I shall be happy to give you any other details which might interest you."

THE STALLION

WALT WHITMAN

A gigantic beauty of a stallion, fresh and responsive to my caress,
Head high in the forehead, wide between the ears,
Limbs glossy and supple, tail dusting the ground,
Eyes full of sparkling wickedness, ears finely cut, flexibly moving.
His nostrils dilate as my heels embrace him,
His well-built limbs tremble with pleasure as we race around and
   return.

A GENUINE MEXICAN PLUG

SAMUEL LANGHORNE CLEMENS

I resolved to have a horse to ride. I had never seen such wild, free, magnificent horsemanship outside of a circus as these picturesquely-clad Mexicans, Californians, and Mexicanized Americans displayed in Carson streets every day. How they rode! Leaning just gently forward out of the perpendicular, easy and nonchalant, with broad slouch-hat brim blown square up in front, and long *riata* swinging above the head, they swept through the town like the wind! The next minute they were only a sailing puff of dust on the far desert. If they trotted, they sat up gallantly and gracefully, and seemed part of the horse; did not go jiggering up and down after the silly Miss-Nancy fashion of the riding-schools. I had quickly learned to tell a horse from a cow, and was full of anxiety to learn more. I was resolved to buy a horse.

While the thought was rankling in my mind, the auctioneer came scurrying through the plaza on a black beast that had as many humps and corners on him as a dromedary, and was necessarily uncomely; but he was "going, going, at twenty-two!—horse, saddle and bridle at twenty-two dollars, gentlemen!" and I could hardly resist.

A man whom I did not know (he turned out to be the auctioneer's brother) noticed the wistful look in my eye, and observed that that was a very remarkable horse to be going at such a price; and added that the saddle alone was worth the money. It was a Spanish saddle, with ponderous *tapidaros*, and furnished with the ungainly sole-leather covering with the unspellable name. I said I had half a notion to bid. Then this keen-eyed person appeared to me to be "taking my measure"; but I dismissed the suspicion when he spoke, for his manner was full of guileless candor and truthfulness. Said he:

"I know that horse—know him well. You are a stranger, I take it, and so you might think he was an American horse, maybe, but I assure you he is not. He is nothing of the kind; but—excuse my speaking in a low voice, other people being near—he is, without the shadow of a doubt, a Genuine Mexican Plug!"

I did not know what a Genuine Mexican Plug was, but there was something about this man's way of saying it, that made me swear inwardly that I would own a Genuine Mexican Plug, or die.

"Has he any other—er—advantages?" I inquired, suppressing what eagerness I could.

He hooked his forefinger in the pocket of my army-shirt, led me to one side, and breathed in my ear impressively these words:

"He can out-buck anything in America!"

"Going, going, going—*twent-ty*-four dollars and a half, gen—"

"Twenty-seven!" I shouted, in a frenzy.

"And sold!" said the auctioneer, and passed over the Genuine Mexican Plug to me.

I could scarcely contain my exultation. I paid the money, and put the animal in a neighboring livery-stable to dine and rest himself.

In the afternoon I brought the creature into the plaza, and certain citizens held him by the head, and others by the tail, while I mounted him. As soon as they let go, he placed all his feet in a bunch together, lowered his back, and then suddenly arched it upward and shot me straight into the air a matter of three or four feet! I came as straight down again, lit in the saddle, went instantly up again, came down almost on the high pommel, shot up again, and came down on the horse's neck—all in the space of three or four seconds. Then he rose and stood almost straight up on his hind feet, and I, clasping his lean neck desperately, slid back into the saddle, and held on. He came down, and immediately hoisted his heels into the air, delivering a vicious kick on the sky, and stood on his fore feet. And then down he came once more, and began the original exercise of shooting me straight up again.

The third time I heard a stranger say: "Oh, *don't* he buck, though!"

While I was up, somebody struck the horse a sounding thwack with a leathern strap, and when I arrived again the Genuine Mexican Plug was not there. A Californian youth chased him up and caught him, and asked if he might have a ride. I granted him that luxury. He mounted the Genuine, got lifted into the air once, but sent his spurs home as he descended, and the horse darted away like a telegram. He soared over three fences like a bird, and disappeared down the road toward the Washoe Valley.

I sat down on a stone with a sigh, and by natural impulse one of my hands sought my forehead, and the other the base of my stomach. I believe I never appreciated, till then, the poverty of the human machinery—for I still needed a hand or two to place elsewhere. Pen cannot describe how I was jolted up. Imagination cannot conceive how disjointed I was—how internally, externally, and universally I was unsettled, mixed up, and ruptured. There was a sympathetic crowd around me though.

One elderly-looking comforter said:

"Stranger, you've been taken in. Everybody in this camp knows that horse. Any child, any Injun, could have told you that he'd buck; he is the very worst devil to buck on the continent of America. You hear *me*. I'm Curry. *Old* Curry. Old *Abe* Curry. And moreover, he is a simon-pure, out-and-out genuine d——d Mexican plug, and an uncommon mean one at that, too. Why, you turnip, if you had laid low and kept dark, there's chances to buy an *American* horse for mighty little more than you paid for that bloody old foreign relic."

I gave no sign; but I made up my mind that if the auctioneer's brother's funeral took place while I was in the Territory I would postpone all other recreations and attend it.

After a gallop of sixteen miles, the California youth and the Genuine Mexican Plug came tearing into town again, shedding foam-flakes like the spume-spray that drives before a typhoon, and, with one final skip over a wheelbarrow and a Chinaman, cast anchor in front of the "ranch."

Such panting and blowing! Such spreading and contracting of the red equine nostrils, and glaring of the wild equine eye! But was the imperial beast subjugated? Indeed, he was not. His lordship the Speaker of the House thought he was, and mounted him to go down to the Capitol; but the first dash the creature made was over a pile of telegraph poles half as high as a church; and his time to the Capitol—one mile and three-quarters—remains unbeaten to this day. But then he took an advantage—he left out the mile, and only did the three-quarters. That is to say, he made a straight cut across lots, preferring fences and ditches to a crooked road; and when the Speaker got to the Capitol he said he had been in the air so much he felt as if he had made the trip on a comet.

In the evening the Speaker came home afoot for exercise, and got the Genuine towed back behind a quartz wagon. The next day I loaned the animal to the Clerk of the House to go down to the Dana silver mine, six miles, and he walked back for exercise, and got the horse towed. Everybody I loaned him to always walked back; they never could get enough exercise any other way. Still, I continued to loan him to anybody who was willing to borrow him, my idea being to get him crippled, and throw him on the borrower's hands, or killed, and make the borrower pay for him. But somehow nothing ever happened to him. He took chances that no other horse ever took and survived, but he always came out safe. It was his daily habit to try experiments that had always before been considered impossible, but he always got through. Sometimes he miscalculated a little, and did not get his rider through intact, but *he* always got through himself. Of course I had tried to sell him; but that was a stretch of simplicity which met with little sympathy. The auctioneer stormed up and down the streets on him for four days, dispersing the populace, interrupting business, and destroying children, and never got a bid—at least never any but the eighteen-dollar one he hired a notoriously substanceless bummer to make. The people only smiled pleasantly, and restrained their desire to buy, if they had any. Then the auctioneer brought in his bill, and I withdrew the horse from the market. We tried to trade him off at private vendue next, offering him at a sacrifice for second-hand tombstones, old iron, temperance tracts—any kind of property. But holders were stiff, and we retired from the market again. I never tried to ride the horse any more. Walking was good enough exercise for a man like me, that had nothing the matter with him except ruptures, internal injuries, and such things. Finally I tried to *give* him away. But it was a failure. Parties said earthquakes were handy enough on the Pacific coast—they did not wish to own one. As a last resort I offered him to the Governor for the use of the "Brigade." His face lit up eagerly at first, but toned down again, and he said the thing would be too palpable.

Just then the livery stable man brought in his bill for six weeks' keeping—stall-room for the horse, fifteen dollars; hay for the horse, two hundred and fifty! The Genuine Mexican Plug had eaten a ton of the article, and the man said he would have eaten a hundred if he had let him.

I will remark here, in all seriousness, that the regular price of hay during that year and a part of the next was really two hundred and fifty dollars a ton. During a part of the previous year it had sold at five hundred a ton, in gold, and during the winter before that there was such scarcity of the article that in several instances small quantities had brought eight hundred dollars a ton in coin! The consequence might be guessed without my telling it: people turned their stock loose to starve, and before the spring arrived Carson and Eagle Valleys were almost literally carpeted with their carcasses! Any old settler there will verify these statements.

I managed to pay the livery bill, and the same day I gave the Genuine Mexican Plug to a passing Arkansas emigrant whom fortune delivered into my hand. If this ever meets his eye, he will doubtless remember the donation.

Now whoever has the luck to ride a real Mexican plug will recognize the animal depicted in this chapter, and hardly consider him exaggerated—but the uninitiated will feel justified in regarding his portrait as a fancy sketch, perhaps.

THE KING IS DEAD

ARTHUR DALEY

The King is dead and he leaves no successor. Man o' War, the mightiest thoroughbred the turf has known, has been affectionately laid to rest beneath the blue grass pastureland where he romped so majestically during his declining years. The veterinarians said that it was a heart attack which caused the death of Big Red. But it could have been a broken heart, too.

Will Harbut had died a few weeks before and Man o' War loved his devoted Negro groom in one of those strange attachments that animals sometimes get for humans. Old Will would coax and baby Big Red. Pridefully he'd reel off the long string of turf accomplishments turned in by his brilliant charge while the beautiful chestnut seemingly would listen and nod knowingly as Old Will described him as "de mostest horse." Then Harbut would plead, "Stand still, Red." And Red would stand still.

Their relationship had been a wonderful one down through the years and the big stallion sorely missed his faithful companion. Perhaps the most touching tribute paid Old Will was in the obituary printed by the official publication of the thoroughbred industry: "Among his survivors are his wife, six sons, three daughters and Man o' War."

Will Harbut wasn't at all extravagant in calling Man o' War the greatest horse of them all. There never was a more remarkable steed. No horse ever stirred the emotions or gripped the imaginations of the public the way Big Red did. He set records almost every time he started and such was his supremacy that he thrice was held at the astronomical odds of 1–to–100, including the classic Belmont Stakes, supposedly the most severe three-year-old test.

He lost only once in his brief racing career; he was upset by Upset as a juvenile. An inexperienced starter sent the field away when Big Red was prancing sideways. He closed like a thunderbolt but finished a half length back.

Only once was he really pressed—disregarding that Upset misadventure—and that was against the lightly weighed John P. Grier. The big chestnut horse, whose coat seemed to shed fire in the sunlight, carried 126 pounds to his rival's 108. They raced together, stride for stride, bobbing head alongside bobbing head, while screaming thousands watched amid mounting excitement. At every furlong pole Man o' War was setting a new record. Into the homestretch they roared and suddenly John P. Grier surged out in front. Man o' War had met his master at long last. Or had he? Will Harbut was right. The "mostest" horse let go with a mighty blast to win by a length and a half. The beaten colt never was as good again.

When Samuel D. Riddle retired Big Red to stud after his three-year-old campaign and after he'd set a then world money-winning record of almost a quarter of a million dollars, Man o' War brought his glamour with him. And he gained even more as his fame as a stallion soared to unbelievable heights. His home at Faraway Farms just outside Lexington became a "must" for every visitor to Kentucky's Blue Grass country.

It was thrilling to see him that regal head lifted imperiously and that powerfully built body shimmering in the sunlight. The rays of the sun darted through the windows over his stall and seemed to fondle the rich, red mane on his neck. He was big, too, at 16.2 hands, a heroic figure of a horse. And he was truly a king in his royal court, condescending to glance with soft brown eyes on the 2,000,000 hero worshipers who made obeisance to his equine majesty. He seemed to sense that he was something above the common plane.

And now Big Red is gone. His like may never be seen again.

The New York Times
November 2, 1947

GATO TAUGHT ME A LESSON

A. F. TSCHIFFELY

When the low houses of Puno had faded away in the distance we came to a range of hills, and after descending the other side we found ourselves on a plain where short, coarse grass grew. Much to my surprise the ground became boggy, but wishing to save time and distance I continued straight towards a cut in the mountain far ahead of us. I knew that this was the way we had to go towards Cuzco, for the Puno-Cuzco railway line went that way, though making a big, sweeping detour. The horses had already waded through soft puddles that gurgled in a very unpleasant way with our weight, and when we came to a broad strip of water which appeared to be traversing the plain from side to side, Gato, whom I was riding, refused to move farther. The water was only some four inches deep, but the horse stopped with the stubbornness of a bad-tempered mule. When I hit him with the lead line he reared up and snorted like a broncho. I tried every means of persuasion to make the horse enter the water, but to no avail. Presently I saw an Indian in the distance who seemed to be shouting and waving his arms as he came running in my direction. When he was near enough I heard him calling to me in broken Spanish to stop. Once he had sufficiently recovered his breath to speak he told me that this was a very dangerous place and that we would meet with disaster if we entered the treacherous pool. He then guided us to a spot far away and put us on a safe trail. Gato had taught me a good lesson, and I never interfered with him again when he refused to step on a doubtful piece of ground. The good old boy had not forgotten the lessons he had learnt in his youth while roaming over the plains of Patagonia. The instincts of the wild horse had warned him that danger was lurking below the innocent-looking water.

It is surprising that neither of the horses was ever badly bogged on the whole trip—more so when it is considered that we went through regions where deadly quicksands and horrible, slimy pools wait to swallow the unfortunate traveller who happens to step into them.

The company of a horse or a dog is a wonderful thing, and with Mancha and Gato I never felt the want of any better. The worry of feeding and looking after them had its recompense, for they helped to pass many hours away that would otherwise have been an empty hell. Usually there was so much to see and to do that the days passed like so many hours, and many a long conversation did I hold with the horses, who were always glad to hear my voice. They learnt to understand quite a few words; thus they would prick up their ears and look around nervously if I asked them "que hay?" (what's up), or they would sniff the air if I said "puma" (South American lion). "Chuck-chuck" meant fodder, and "agua" water, and these they knew as well as a baby does "daddy" and "mummy." If I happened to say, "vamos, vamos," they woke up and stepped out faster, and a slow "bueno" never had to be repeated to make them stop.

By this time the horses and myself were the best of friends, or "amadrinado" as the gauchos call it. The bell-mare of a "tropilla" (troop) is called "madrina" in the Argentine, from which noun this pretty adjective "amadrinado" is derived. In order to appreciate fully the friendship of a horse, a man has to live in the open with him for some time. As soon as the animal comes to a region that is strange to him he will never go away from his master but will look for his company and in case of danger seek his protection. By this time both my horses were so fond of me that I never had to tie them again, and even if I slept in some lonely hut I simply turned them loose at night, well knowing that they would never go more than a few yards away and that they would be waiting for me at the door in the early morning, when they always greeted me with a friendly nicker.

going   fight, and down country she went,
hers   pping.

A   kept my distance. But the fun wasn't
over   d, for getting the both in the delapidated   some miles and at the edge of the
wash,   dest to do. The short wings of the
corral   one, and to make it still more ticklish
there   ot coating of ice at the only gate, all
over th   t it a ways. That ice had formed from
a spring above it,   mp and corral seldom being used, the
run of the water from it took its own course.

There was a small shed at one side of the corral where the
supposed-to-be poor cow and calf was to be put and it was up to
me to put 'em there.

Being I hadn't crowded the cow none while she and her calf
hightailed down the wash, only to get a glimpse of 'em once in a
while and see that they was going right, they was sort of calmed
down some when she reached the place to where I was to turn
'em towards the corral.

The cow turned easy enough and went on peaceful, until she
came to the corral and the ice, and then, as I'd expected, her calf of
a sudden broke away and the cow also whirled to make a dash for
a break. Expecting that, I of course had my loop ready. I had her
too close now to let her get away. I piled it onto her as she tried to
run past, at the same time put Joker to speed on thru the corral
gate, forgetting about the coating of ice and his getting any footing there. But with the speed we went there was no stopping, and
being there was quite a slope inside the corral there was nothing
for the cow to do but swap ends and follow. The shed was at the
lower end of the corral. The cow, now on the fight, even tho she
was sliding down on her side piled up in the shed, right with me
and Joker, all on our sides.

There was a crash, bang against the log wall of the shed as the three of us hit it all in one heap. With watching the cow's horns and the slack of my rope so I wouldn't get tangled up in it, I was pretty busy, and so was Joker, for he didn't want to be in such close quarters with that mad cow and her horns. When we all crashed into the log wall, there was enough impact so that it broke some and Joker went on halfways thru. He done the rest in getting all the way thru.

He'd got his footing from the falling logs, bark and all there was under the shed, and left me there with the cow. I didn't want her to go thru the same hole we made, so, I dodged her horns and tied her down before she could get up, with the same rope I'd caught her with and forgot it was still hard and fast to the saddle horn.

Joker no more than got out of the shed when on slick ice he again lost his footing and slid on his side plum to the end of the rope, drawing it tight, and now he couldn't get his feet under him so as to get up. So there he was on the outside and down, and the cow inside also down.

I had a hard time standing up myself as I went along the rope to him, and the rope being so tight I seen where the only way he could get up was to uncinch the saddle and let him slide away from it to where he could get his footing.

He looked kind of foolish after that was done and finally got to his feet again. But the only joke there was on him that time was how he sure wasn't going to bed down with that mad cow crowding him so close, and then afterwards hitting the end of the rope and get "busted" (thrown) so he couldn't get up.

Both cow and horse now taken care of, I made an opening in a bare part of the corral and didn't have too much trouble getting the calf in. But I was sure to change the course of that spring water right afterwards. The ice soon got soft then and in a couple of days the most of it had melted away, leaving the corral more fit to use again.

It was in that same corral some days later when Joker, acting funny, took another bust. For having nothing to do as it was, with all the good hay he could eat, he got to feeling more rollicky than ever, if that was possible, for he always was full of the old nick plenty of snorts.

This time I was going to catch him, figuring to ride to another spring, more to pass the time away than thinking there'd be any stock there that would need attention. I tried to stop him so I could walk up to him but there was no chance there. I made a few tries, and seeing there was nothing doing that way I went and got my rope.

Feeling as good as he did, the sight of my rope with ready loop, acted sort of like a fuse in the dynamite that was in him, and before I could get within throwing distance of him he just sort of bounced, like a spooked antelope, and hit for the delapidated but tall corral gate— He hit it plum center and high, but not clearing it, and with the force and speed he hit it the gate crashed to splinters. At the same time, his knees caught on the top pole which upended him to land quite a ways and to a mighty hard fall.

It all happened so quick that all I done was stand in the corral with sudden thought that there I was without a horse, afoot, for, knowing his tricks as I did, I figured he'd jump right up and hightail it down country. There was only one fence in that part of the desert country and that was the corral fence, then it was all open (and still is) till the next corral miles away was reached, no pastures.

But to my surprise, when Joker jumped up, looked around kind of dazed and then spotted me inside the corral, he bowed his neck and jumped right back over the gate he'd splintered just a few seconds before, and into the corral again, shook his head, and snorting, stopped to within a few feet of me, facing and watching. He'd thought me responsible for the fall he'd just had, and that he'd get another if he tried to break away from me again.

Where he'd got that education was that, along with other happenings we'd had, and the one of just a few days before where he'd took such a slide and hard fall, he'd come to thinking he'd only get the worst of it by trying to break away. He stood quivering, but plum still then as I walked up to him and slipped my rope over his head.

I was at that camp about a week when I took it onto myself to turn that cow and calf out and shove 'em to a country where they belonged. Where they ought to've been in the first place. Then I rode on to the main camp where I took on a fresh string of horses and went to riding from other spring camps, where a rider was really needed.

But I kept Joker in with the new string, and I was riding him along one day when I run onto a lanky steer with one horn grown bent and which was gouging into his upper jaw. That steer had been missed in quite a few round-ups or that horn would have been taken care of.

I soon seen why he'd been missed, for he run alone, and soon as he seen me he was gone like a deer, hitting for a thick patch of that brushy country. But this time he was some distance too far away from it, and before he could get to it my loop caught up with him.

But not as I wanted it to, for instead of catching him by his one straight horn and the head as I intended, the loop sailed down alongside his nose and caught him by one front foot. I didn't know I'd caught him until I pulled up on my slack, and then things happened.

It was an accident and one of the queer ones that happens with roping, but at the speed we all was going down the steep side hill, and I pulling up my slack, that steer upended to a clean turn over. He upended a second time and then as he got to scrambling to his feet, all with no let up in the speed, and neither Joker nor me expecting any such, Joker run right onto that steer's upraised rump, turning him over once more, and as that steer turned over again, Joker and me was also very much upraised by his frame, like from

"JOKER"

(A Horse That Lived Up to His Name)

WILL JAMES

Joker had already been named such before he was turned over to me, and a joker he sure turned out to be. For a horse he could get himself into more predicaments that would wind up into jokes on himself, including his rider, than most humans do.

He was a young horse, had been rode only a few times when I slipped my rope on him and went to work for the desert cow outfit he belonged to. I'd hired out to ride for that outfit and, as the joker horse he was, he fooled me the first time I laid eyes on him.

The foreman was in the corral with me, pointing out the string of horses another rider had started breaking and I was to finish. Joker was one of 'em, a mighty well set up and good size blood bay, and running and snorting around the way he was, drawed my attention to him more than did the others.

Being a stranger in that country and wanting to make a sort of acquainting conversation with the foreman I asked him how much that Joker horse would weigh. He answered: "Make a guess."

It might be hard for some to believe but in some of the range countries, sometimes only a hundred miles or so separating, a horse of the same size and appearance will vary from one to two hundred pounds in weight, sometimes more. That's due to the kind of feed different ranges produce, also climate. Many an experienced horse dealer is fooled by the weight of a horse on that account, also by their age, for a horse from sandy, dry and brushy ranges will show a younger mouth than the one from the tall grass ranges and where running water is a-plenty.

As I've already said, Joker was a well set up and good sized horse and I made my guess according to the many such size and built horses I'd handled on other ranges. After I'd caught and walked up to him I guessed him to weigh eleven hundred.

The foreman grinned some. "I weighed him at the stockyards just a few days ago," he says, "and with saddle and all he weighed nine hundred and twenty."

Well, that was one at my expense from Joker.

It was on the next day when one of Joker's jokes turned on him. I'd made all ready the day before to hit out with a string of eight broncs, with only one gentle horse for pack and snubbing. The foreman had left me alone at the desert cow camp, figuring on making another such camp across a stretch of thirty miles and no water between (no distance for an automobile but no such country where an automobile could move).

To be sure of making that distance, along with driving my string of broncs, I picked on one in the string which I figured would have the age, and be hard and tough enough to stand up under the long and dry ride.

After the job of saddling and topping this horse, making it as I could so's to save him and myself, I opened the corral gate to start out with my string, the only gate from there to the camp I was headed for.

My string came out of the corral quiet enough, and then, a short distance down a dry wash, and all going well, this Joker horse of a sudden broke loose and like a bullet hit straight out for the horse range, where I'd got him from with the others just the day before.

There was no chance of heading him off. I tried but the horse I was riding "bogged" his head (went to bucking) and then stampeded another direction, no stopping him.

After finally circling him towards where my string had been, they'd also started, and going another direction from where I wanted 'em to go. With my horse now some winded, I manoeuvred him so's to turn 'em. As good luck would have it, they'd stayed together, Joker being the only one missing and now very much out of sight. I had to let him go, figuring I would get him a month or so later, when I'd get back to the main camp again.

But such wasn't to be, not according to Joker, and along about the heat of noon that same day there come a streak of dust, and a blood bay horse making it. It was Joker. He'd made a circle of the horse range, looking for a bunch he was used to running with, and not finding it, had returned to the string, for there was two in the string that had belonged to the same bunch.

Joker had made quite a circle and covered more than a few miles by then, and he was good to stay with the string, behaving well until camp was reached. His wild break away had turned out to be a wild goose chase and a sort of joke. To his expense this time.

Another joke at his expense was when the foreman of this same outfit rode up to my camp and said that the owner (a mining man who knew a lot about ore and holes in the ground but nothing about cattle) ordered him to have me move to another spring camp and run in what he thought was a weak cow he'd drove by and seen standing in the middle of a big dry and high mesa flat, with a calf by her side, dying of thirst, he thought, and starving.

I was having my hands full with quite a few hundred head of mighty scattered cattle at the time, and the mention of having me move to another camp to take care of just one lone cow and calf, more than made me and the foreman wonder and laugh some.

But orders was orders, and I sure didn't mind such an order because I'd been riding mighty hard for some time. Another rider took my place and my string, all but Joker. I figured he'd be just the horse I'd need for that lone and easy job, for, with his funny and tricky ways he'd sort of keep me company.

The time being winter and no stock running in that higher country, the owner had some grub and baled hay freighted some fifty miles in to the camp for just me, Joker and cow and calf. That and my time alone cost more than the cow was worth but that wasn't considered, nor any of my business, and right then I figured I'd have some easy riding for some days, at least until the owner of the outfit found out that all the cow needed was a good shove down country where she belonged.

The first day of my expected easy riding didn't start so good —I found the cow. She wasn't exactly in prime shape for beef. If she had been she'd been easier to handle, and as she was, she was just in good shape to fight, and her husky calf was right aching for a good run.

The cow was pretty wild, and being alone with her calf that way, and the sight of a rider coming up on her, done everything but make her any tamer. I seen right away I'd have trouble getting that old heifer to the corral where I was to feed her, and I took her as easy as possible, staying a good distance away and not turning her any more often than I could help, for, by her actions she just wanted an excuse to get on the fight, and one turn or two too many would be sure to set her off.

I let her amble on pretty well as she pleased for a ways, and being I'd started her right, she headed on near the direction of the corral, only kind of at an angle. I let her amble on that direction for a ways, figuring on turning her when reaching the head of a dry wash which started from the mesa, wound thru the jack pine and led on down to near where the corral was.

Spooky cattle often take to down country well, especially a wash, and if the rider sort of keeps out of sight they'll sure ramble on in trying to lose him and not try to "brush" on him.

Joker was working good, and when the right time come I spurted him onto her so sudden that she just like sort of fell off the rim and into the head of the wash without looking where she was

Dandy tucked into his nose-bag greedily. The mare would not look at hers.

"Come on, missus," said Humbleton.

He warmed some water, making a weak gruel, sprinkled bran on the top, and held the bucket to her nostrils temptingly.

She breathed on it, her breath mingling with the steam, but would not touch it.

The Colonel walked round her with anxious eyes, pulled her ears, hand-rubbed her cold pasterns.

It's that wood, he thought.

Then he rummaged in his multitudinous pockets. After long search he produced a thermometer and took her temperature.

It was 103, and there was still a twenty-mile march before them.

He got her a ball and gave it her.

There was no stabling at the *estaminet;* and nothing for it therefore but to go on.

He swung into his saddle again.

The track lay before them invisible save for the half-obliterated furrows left by the gun-wheels. The snow came waving across them in white curtains that almost seemed to lighten the darkness. The moustaches of both men froze and were thatched with snow. The two white-cloaked figures laboured along side by side like two phantom horsemen with feet of lead.

The mare seemed to come on a little better.

Every now and then the Colonel said—

"How's she feel now?"

And Humbleton answered—

"Very queer, sir."

At length they came to the foot of a long bare ridge, stretching interminably before them, smooth and bleak and white as a shroud, great curtains of snow flapping dismally across its desolate face.

The mare stopped.

Both men dismounted. The Colonel with a hoot-picker, disengaged with difficulty from a remote interior pocket, emptied her hoofs of the balling snow.

He thought she was going to lie down; and once she lay down on that slope he knew he would never get her up again.

He and Humbleton, crouching in the snow, hand-rubbed her legs and flanks. Then they started leading her up the slope.

The two men were wonderfully kind and patient with the suffering creature; far more kind and patient with her than with each other.

The forlorn little group toiled desolately up the slope, now engulfed in a billow of waving white, now emerging into blotted dimness, the wind rollicking away with terrible laughter in the valley below. The horses, with windy tails tucked-in and strewn about their flanks, plodded on with downward heads, shaking the snow from their ears like big dogs with a rattle of accoutrements that sounded weirdly in the night.

Honest and kind as always, the mare was doing her dumb best; and both men knew it. One on either side, they shouldered her up the slope, easing her, halting her, talking to her, coaxing her on a step at a time, as a nurse teaching a child to walk. And every now and then she rubbed her snowy head against one man or the other, as though recognizing their love, and wishing to tell them about it.

Somehow or other they bolstered her up to the top of that Ridge of Windy Death.

Down in the valley, on the other side, the Colonel hoped he might find a Cavalry Division, and some shelter for the mare.

He was right.

As they descended the slope, the mare walking more easily, they found themselves among friends.

The Gunners were in possession of the valley.

Officers and men with lanterns came to the rescue. Most of them knew the Colonel; many of them the mare. A veterinary surgeon was found and pulled out of his bed. The mare was given a roomy box in a farm. She revived somewhat. Willing hands bedded her down in bracken. Humbleton set to work to warm and dry her. The Colonel took her temperature and found it less.

The light was just stealing over the white-bosomed hills and snow-thatched roofs when he swung into the saddle to ride the last long stage to his Headquarters alone.

The mare was playing with some hay, and Humbleton was rugging her up, as he left her.

IV

All that day he was busy, and no news came through; but a horse of his Orderly Officer died partly from exposure and partly from eating wood, the vet. said.

Next morning early the Colonel rode off to the valley where the mare was to see how things were going.

As he rode up to the yard of the farm, Humbleton, looking in his goat-skin like a little clean-shaven Robinson Crusoe, came ploughing through the snow to meet him.

He looked very dogged and did not catch the Colonel's eye.

"Well?" said the Colonel.

"Mare's dead, sir," answered the little man.

"Indeed!" said the Colonel rudely. "What time?"

"Two o'clock this morning."

The Colonel said nothing and dismounted.

Heavily he walked through the slush of the farmyard towards the loose-box and entered.

Honest and kind in death as in life, the brown mare lay on her side, rough of coat, her long neck stretched out, her long flat thin legs slightly crooked, her shoes upturned and shining, looking strangely pathetic.

Over head Humbleton had scrawled in chalk upon a beam:

Kitty:
Died for her country
1 *March*, 1916

The Colonel stood above her.

He was glad she had such a thick bed of bracken to rest upon.

Then he bent and felt her heart.

One of those strange and overwhelming waves of emotion, of which we cannot trace the origin, came surging up out of the inland ocean of his being and choked him.

He kicked the bracken about with his feet, and blew his nose.

Then he said—

"We shall miss her, Humbleton."

The little groom, standing in his goat-skin jacket in the door, his back towards his master, looked out over the snow and answered nothing.

Tried in that white-hot furnace, Guardsmen and gunners proved worthy of each other and of the traditions of their great regiments. There was no rest by night or day for officers, men, or horses.

Kitty, the mare, took it all very calmly. Back with the limbers, on the sheltered side of the ridge on which the guns were barking, she stretched her long neck, bowed a knee, and grazed the Flemish turf at ease much as on Salisbury Plain. The hubbub across the ridge, her master's fierce peremptory voice, the occasional burst of shrapnel near by, disturbed her little.

Now and then the trumpeter, handing over the mare and his own horse to the care of Humbleton, would crawl to the top of the ridge and watch the Battery in action beyond, pounding away at the greycoats struggling in the valley. He didn't see much: for the guns were roughly dug in. But once he saw a farmhouse which the Major was using for observation post crash down in headlong ruin.

"Gosh!" muttered the trumpeter. "Spotted 'im. He's done."

Then the long, lean Major came running out of the dust and debris.

The trumpeter returned at the trot to his horses.

"Old man ain't 'alf nippy," he reported to Humbleton.

"He ain't so old neether, then," answered Humbleton, who took no liberties with his master himself, and allowed none.

"Ain't he, then," retorted the trumpeter who must have the last word even in the mouth of Hell. "I'll lay he's older than he were twenty year ago, then."

Once on that last desperate day, when the one skeleton Cavalry Brigade held in reserve was dashing here and there to make good as best it might gaps in the broken line, the Major got his guns up under a wall to cover the Guards' counter-attack launched as a forlorn hope. The Germans saw him and swept the wall away with a tidal wave of fire.

It was *Rear limber up!* and the gun-teams came up at the gallop.

In the hubbub and tumult of shells, shouts, of gunners furiously handling gun-wheels, of drivers with outstretched whip-hands quieting their teams, of bloody men disengaging bloody and floundering horses, Kitty, the mare, was steady as a rock.

"Got her, sir?" gasped the trumpeter, as he toppled off his own horse.

"Right," said the Major, toe in his stirrup, and swung into his saddle. *"Battery column, gallop!"*

And somehow or other the Battery swung clear.

Those were astounding days. For three weeks the officers and men of that Battery never had their clothes off, and for days together the horses were never unharnessed. But whoever else went short Kitty, the mare, never suffered. Humbleton saw to that, and to be just the mare saw to herself in her large and sensible way, grazing when opportunity offered, and snatching *bonne bouches* from ruined haystacks.

After the first terrible six weeks the Armies settled down to trench warfare. It was not the game for Horse Artillery; but the Black Horse Battery played it with zest all through that first winter.

The horses stood out in the open and thrived. Kitty grew a coat like a bear's; and the saddle sank into her back as into a drift of brown snow. But campaigning suited her as it did her black companion Dandy.

Then came promotion.

The Major, now a Brevet-Lieutenant-Colonel, took command of a Field Artillery Brigade. That did not last for long. Within a few weeks he and Humbleton and the two horses were back with the Horse Artillery, the Colonel now commanding a Brigade.

III

The Headquarters of the Brigade was in a chateau some thirty miles behind the firing line.

When the turn of the Cavalry Division, to which the Brigade

was attached, came for a spell in the trenches, horses and guns made a long forced march by night and took up their positions early in December of the second winter of the War.

They had three months in the trenches—months of sleet and rain, of dogged endurance, infinitely dull, varied by lurid nightmare interludes.

When towards the end of February they were relieved nobody in the Division regretted it.

That was the time of the heavy snows; and all reliefs were made of necessity at night.

The Horse Artillery started for the thirty-mile trek home at midnight, the long thin line of guns, their wheels thick with snow, trailing worm-like through the white dimness that muffled the noise of their going and made the procession strangely ghost-like.

Wagons and kits were to follow later.

The Colonel gave his Brigade an hour's start.

It was just one when his batman came to the door of his much-shelled lodging and announced that Humbleton and the horses were outside.

The Colonel, busy destroying papers, went to the door, accompanied by his terrier Bruiser. The little groom, in his goat-skin coat, stood outside in the snow, the horses in hand. Dandy stretched a neck to greet his little friend, the terrier, standing three-legged, and shivering in the snow, while the mare nibbled tentatively at a pile of wood close by.

"Don't let her eat that!" ordered the Colonel ferociously.

He always spoke to his servants as if they were his mortal enemies and he wished them to know he knew it. And they took more from him than they would have done from many a man with a smoother tongue and a smaller heart. It was just the old man's way, they said among themselves. And he had the qualities which ensured respect if they did not win love. He was just, consistent, and in the heart of him considerate. So, to the surprise of many, they always stuck to him.

The Colonel went back to his room with Bruiser, and piled on layer upon layer of clothes: sweaters, hunting-waistcoats, Norfolk jackets, towards the top a suit of oilskins, and over all a Burberry.

In multitudinous pockets he stuffed an electric torch, a flask, a thermos, a map, a ball of string, an extra pair of gloves, a muffler, and other odds and ends. The lean Colonel, now a very portly man, gave certain curt instructions to his batman, tied Bruiser, who was to follow with the kits, to the leg of the table, and mounted Dandy: for he knew of old that the mare was not clever in the snow.

Then he set off into the night, Humbleton and the mare following in his wake.

Once clear of the village the Colonel looked round. In that little distance he had already gained greatly on the other pair.

He waved for the groom to come up alongside.

"Leg her up," he ordered gruffly. "Keep her alongside me."

Side by side master and man rode along through the night, the snow coating them heavily.

"She's walking abominably," said the Colonel.

"Yes, sir," answered Humbleton, who never wasted words, least of all on his master.

Laboriously the Colonel disengaged his electric torch and flashed it on the mare.

What he saw he didn't like.

The snow was heavy on her shoulders, thick in her ears, plastering her heavy coat; and she was slouching along disconsolately, her head down, as though smelling out a track.

It's that wood poisoned her, thought the Colonel; but he didn't say anything.

"Does she feel all right?" he asked.

"Yes, sir," answered Humbleton.

Twelve miles out they stopped at a little *estaminet* for a water and feed.

his racing days were over I rode Billy on the garden, eventually pensioning him off. He died peacefully of old age. Those of us who know the Indian bazaar horse-dealer know how much that meant.

THE BROWN MARE

ALFRED OLLIVANT

He used to bring her home when he came on his winter's leave in the years before the War, to hunt with the South Down; for she was an unusually fine performer across country. And it was there I met her.

A tall upstanding creature, sixteen hands and over, very high at the withers, not quite clean-bred and yet showing breeding in every line. She did not really carry bone enough for the heavy Wealden clay, in which your horse sinks up to his hocks at every stride; but the Major was clearly always pleased when the big iron-gray Granite had strained a sinew and he could fall back on the mare for an extra day. And little Humbleton, the very British groom, with the blue eyes, the chestnut hair, and stolid way, was just the same. When exercising, he always rode the mare for preference and led the gray. She was honest and she was kind, with the heart of a woman and the manners of a lady. Yet except for a general air of breeding I do not think you would have singled her out in a crowd.

Kitty came first into the Major's stable when after a long spell at the War Office he went back to regimental work and took over the command of Field Battery. I think he picked her out of the ranks; maybe the trumpeter had been riding her.

In that stable other horses came and went. The mare stayed; and her reputation grew.

At the big Aldershot meeting the Major entered her for the

Artillery Point-to-point. He was never hard on his horses, and didn't ride her out. She was not placed. Afterwards he heard the whole Brigade had been backing her.

When the Major got his Jacket and took command of the Black Horse Battery at the Wood, Humbleton and the mare went with him. She was not black: she was brown. Therefore he could not ride her on ceremonial parades as his first charger. So he bought a sporting little black horse with a short back, Dandy by name, on which he rode with nodding plume at the head of his Troop down Park Lane, across Piccadilly and the Mall, to fire salutes on Horse Guards Parade.

But if she was no longer his first charger she was still first in his heart; and for long days on Salisbury Plain during autumn manoeuvres she had not her equal.

There followed three quiet years of preparation, the Black Horse Battery doing the Musical Drive at Olympia, swirling at the gallop in rhythmic figures interlaced about the famous bronze Gundamuck gun which the Troop had lost when covering the retreat from Cabul in the first Afghan War and recovered forty years later in the second. The Battery drove to the admiration of connoisseurs, artists, and the London crowd; and then would march down to Salisbury Plain to break records there in the mimic business of war.

Then came the reality; and the Major had to make the sacrifice of his life, and break up in a moment the fighting unit which through three laborious years he had trained to the point of perfection. Immediately on mobilization he was called upon to send all his horses, all his men, and half his officers to complete the strength of a first-for-service Battery at Aldershot. He stood with folded arms on the barrack-square and watched the famous black teams, shining in the sun and beloved of Londoners, file out of the gate. The subalterns said they thought the Major's heart would break. It was perhaps a little comfort to him that when horses and men arrived at Aldershot the Major of the first-for-service Battery there asked his own gun-team drivers to give place to the new-comers.

"These are the drivers of the Black Horse Troop," he said.

The only men left the Major were Humbleton and his batman; the only horses Dandy and the mare. For the rest he had his guns; his non-commissioned officers; a couple of subalterns, reservists, and the pick of all the horses that were streaming into London with which to build up a new Battery.

II

He had two months in which to do it; and he did it.

In those days there was no tarrying. The Germans were knocking at the Gates of Calais.

At the beginning of October the Black Horse Battery, its horses no longer black, many-coloured, many-cornered, but a hard and handy crowd, disembarked at Zeebrugge with the Seventh Division in the romantic and desperate endeavour to relieve Antwerp; and the officers of the Guards Brigade to which the Battery was attached muttered among themselves that if it was no longer the Battery of Olympia days it was still the best Horse Battery in England.

Antwerp fell the day they landed. The Immortal Division, 20,000 strong, marched out to meet the enemy much as David went to meet Goliath. In a perilously thin-drawn-out line it flung itself across the path of the German herds driving bull-headed, hundred thousands of them, for the sea and the island that lay across the Channel.

General French sent word to the valiant Division that he would reinforce them in five hours. Those reinforcements took five days to come. But the Division held; though at the end of the stress it had but forty officers left out of the four hundred who had disembarked at Zeebrugge six weeks before.

In those tremendous days Black Horse Battery played its fiery part in support of the First Battalion of the Grenadier Guards.

restrain him, the more vicious became his assaults on the bottom of the trap, and in a very short time he had half the floor boards splintered and littering the track. My friend ceased his deep breathing exercises and returned somewhat to his senses convinced that it was an earthquake. I told him rather sharply to pull himself together, because in a very few moments we should be leaving the buggy.

I had no intention of continuing down the blind cutting with Mustard Pot in his present frame of mind, and as clearly as possible I tried to drum this into my companion's bemused head, also that the horse had more or less bolted; and that if I failed to master him before reaching the river our best plan would be to roll over the side of the buggy as compactly as possible. The barricade suddenly loomed up stark and threatening out of the mist ahead, and as I managed with a great effort to steer the beast down the sharp declivity to the right, I shouted lustily to my companion to jump, dropped the reins, and quietly heaved myself over the splashboard into the ditch.

I still think that he was under the impression that we had arrived home, that all he had to do was to step out of the buggy, and that the violent jolting was just one of those purely internal affairs of his own. At all events, instead of acting with the briskness the occasion merited, he stood up unsteadily on the few remaining floor boards and attempted to lower himself gently over the side, his foot in search of the elusive foot-rest, which by this time was not there. Failing to discover any foothold for his rocking form, he suddenly disappeared from view beneath the wheels of the racing buggy as it lurched drunkenly down the slope.

Freeing myself with some difficulty from the dense jungle of the deep road-side drain that had broken my fall, I went in anxious search of the buggy's other two occupants, muffled groans leading me in the direction where at least one of them had fallen. There I discovered my friend, who, judging by the noise he was making, seemed to be in a very bad way, and I cursed myself, not forgetting

Mustard Pot, for running him into such a predicament. Apparently he had been run over by both wheels, one passing over his chest, bruising his ribs, while the other had taken one of his ankles, which appeared to be badly sprained. He was quite unable to walk, and after he had regained some of the breath that had been so unkindly knocked out of him, I left him sitting despondently in the mist and went off in search of some sort of conveyance to carry him home. Of the syce there was no trace, and I concluded he was either dead or already at home with Mustard Pot.

There were a few native huts in a clearing near-by, and after wakening the sleeping occupants and convincing them that I was human and not an apparition, I persuaded four of the men to accompany me, bringing one of their light string-beds to carry my injured friend the remaining three miles home. He refused to have anything further to do with buggies.

On the way home we discovered the syce sitting nursing his bruises beside what remained of the trap. Apparently he had clung to his oscillating perch until it had stopped, or, to be more exact, until that portion to which he belonged had come to a standstill; for Mustard Pot, finding himself in complete control, and kicking like a fiend to free himself, had gone on with the shafts. When we arrived home with our stretcher case a good hour afterwards, we discovered him patiently waiting to be admitted into his warm loose-box, and I was glad to find him none the worse.

That was not by any means the only time I had chosen the lesser of two evils by rolling out of the trap, but the horse had always managed to arrive with the empty buggy more or less intact.

Returning home once on one of these lonely drives through the darkness, with Mustard Pot behaving himself and going fast and well, and myself under the influence of a good dinner and good company, I became drowsy, and painfully returned to my sense by the roadside amidst a shower of sparks. It slowly dawned on me that my syce, who had also taken a purler, but a more gentle one than mine, was binding a puggri tightly round my head, and that my face was covered with blood. Swinging down an incline at our accustomed homing speed one of the wheels had struck half a tree-trunk that must have fallen from a passing cart that afternoon. Knowing the road to be in good repair, I had not been quite so wakeful as usual, and the impact had pitched me into a pile of rocks. Mustard Pot had gone on, naturally, leaving the syce and myself to walk the remaining miles through tiger and leopard in-fested jungle as best we could. I managed it without falling by the wayside, and, as usual, found the horse, still between the shafts, awaiting us and quietly demanding his evening ration of oats.

The doctor babu dressed and plastered up my wounds until the following morning, when the medico arrived and added to the general discomfort by stitching my head together again in several places, and counselling bed for three days' rest. Another piece of advice he quite unnecessarily tendered me was either to sell Mus-tard Pot or in future only use him as a hack, or one day I would undoubtedly break my neck. After one or two other occasions in which acrobatics played a leading part, and after seriously weigh-ing up the pros and cons of our career together, for I was very fond of the old beast, I reluctantly decided to pass him on to a friend of mine who needed a good hack, but only on the under-standing that he was never again placed between a pair of shafts. The old horse—he is an old horse now—is still doing his daily dozen round the work of the plantation; and if looks count for anything and one or two splints are ignored, there still remain a good many years of useful service ahead of him. But I hope he has long forgotten how to trap!

And so they came, stayed a while, and passed on. I had several others, some good, some indifferent, but never a bad one, and they were all stout friends.

Souvenir replaced Mustard Pot and taught me much about polo. He it was, too, who introduced me to the thrills of racing, and he won a number of cups for me over the shorter distances. I had him for eight years, and except when he once over-reached himself in a paper chase he was never sick or sorry—a great horse.

Racing led me into acquiring Billy, a hard-mouthed little Bhutan hill pony. A friend of mine joined in the venture and bought another of this same Himalayan breed. We trained Billy and Marquis together, and won several races.

The great difficulty was to keep them confined to the small and restricted circular tracks of the racecourse. A good deal of schooling and training was necessary, and it was no small part of the jockey's task to finish a race by passing the post, and not in an entirely different direction. We used to train our two little grey flyers in great secrecy for six weeks before the races were due to begin, as much to accustom the lightweight jockey to their short stride as to teach the ponies to gallop within the confines of the beflagged course. Since the various districts were cut off from each other by forest and rivers, we never knew the capabilities of the entries until the races took place, and we were always eager to spring a surprise on some of our rivals. We used to run our Bhutias against each other every day in the cool of the evening, over a measured course round the outskirts of our polo field, under conditions similar to those they would experience on the racecourse. Each run was timed, and towards the end of their training we speeded them up into their best galloping form until the day of the races, when we knew that any other Bhutia that expected to leave them behind would have to move. We had to arrange for horse-boxes in advance and entrain our ponies; for these race meetings took place sixty miles away, and were always a great occasion with many shirts lost on the totalisator. Men backed their own club or district favourites, and anybody who could enter a 'dark horse' generally swept the pool.

Our two little Bhutias ran right well for us on every occasion, taking quite a load of rupees from the 'tote,' until they became so handicapped that to run them was too weighty an affair. When and a playful pressure of the hand just behind the saddle always resulted in a first-class imitation of a bucking bronco.

She initiated me into the glorious game of polo, and we had many years on the field together. With me she played a perfect game, but when a stranger took her out for a chukker she never failed to shy off the ball at the moment of impact, pulling the whole time like a fiend, or she would take him completely off the field in one of her non-stop gallops. Her rider, after taking part in every evolution but that of striking the ball, was relieved when the gong sounded the end of the chukker.

The mare and I had many a painful spill together, but generally she managed to come off scot-free, or nearly so, and was polo-sound until the day she died. Not so I, who had some unlucky days. My teeth were smashed, collar bone broken, and a couple of cracked ribs once prevented me from laughing for two whole months. She was a game little lady, and many a cup I won with her. Besides polo, she jumped well, raced occasionally, and once we took the cup from a strong field over a reconnaissance course of twenty-two miles, through rice lands, river beds, scrub, and forest. I used her less strenuously as her years advanced, but she was an affectionate and bonny pony until the end, when she failed to come through an anaesthetic while in the hands of the vet. Stout-hearted old Jill.

Before that came Wilkie. He too was grey, a full-blooded 14.2 Arab, fast and handy on the polo field, but a terrible stumbling-block as a hack and lacking Jill's versatility. Although somewhat past his heyday Wilkie could certainly play polo, but since the greater part of his active life had been spent on the polo field, all he understood was a hand canter or a thundering gallop—I never knew him to trot. His legs were of little use to him anywhere but on grass as flat as a lawn, and in a couple of years they gave out altogether.

My next delve into the market produced the never-to-be-forgotten Mustard Pot, and with him Bush Girl, a couple of English-bred gees that had spent most of their life in India with the artillery. When the regiment left the country, the pick of their horses was disposed of, and as they were going remarkably cheap, there was an invasion of them into the tea districts, and I, among many others, decided to have a couple. They turned up trumps. Mustard Pot was a big raking chestnut gelding standing 15.3, and the mare, Bush Girl, at 14.3, promised, after some schooling, to develop into a first-class polo pony. She was just the handy size, short barrelled, quick off the mark, and with a mouth like silk.

Mustard Pot, owing principally to some of the nightmare drives he has given me, will always retain a lasting place in my memory. He was much too big and unwieldy for the polo field, but with the early schooling he had gone through with the artillery, he turned out to be a fast and capable trapper. To ensure that his abilities in this direction should not be wasted, or go to seed through want of practice, I hunted round and bought a second-hand buggy to keep him company. It was just as well that I had not gone in for a more expensive turnout, for the trap had not then been built that Mustard Pot could not have put the word 'finis' to when he felt inclined. He was a perfect, long-striding hack and untiring across country, taking bunds, ditches, and dykes in his fast and powerful stride without the least exertion. Pulling the light buggy was mere child's play to one who had been with the game.

A reliable horse at all other times, Mustard Pot had a rooted objection to late nights. Then he had to be handled with much circumspection and considerable skill. Even when being yoked into the buggy preparatory to the long homeward run, he was quite prepared to leave it standing, and it was an effort on the part of the syce and myself to get him between the shafts and hitched up at all. Seldom, if ever, did he give us time to settle comfortably into our seats. The syce stood at his head, both hands on the bit, while I collected the reins and held on to the trap. With a nimble

jump to one side the syce would let go, and Mustard Pot, rising
on his hind-legs with a mighty pull, would be off at once in top
gear. In the meantime I had sprung dexterously towards the
driving-seat; the syce, with a precision gained through much practice, would make a dive, for his perch at the rear as the buggy
shot past him, and there would be no stopping Mustard Pot until
he reached home.

There was never any check to his long raking trot through the
mist and darkness; up-hill or down, the gradient meant little to
him. With an easy feel of the mouth, I trusted in his road sense
and my own lucky star, and mile after mile of jungle road dropped
rapidly behind us. Mustard Pot, in his own powerful way, had
much horse sense, and could always be relied upon to keep the
middle of the road and take his corners wide, but never when in
one of his 'get-a-move-on' moods would he tolerate a tightening
or pulling of the reins. If he ever broke from his mile-eating trot
to the canter, I was always to blame, and his night sight being far
superior to my own, his mouth was generally left severely alone.
As soon as I tried to ease or slow him up, he accepted the challenge, and fought me for the bit; and if I still persisted, he would
arch his beautiful neck and break into a canter, raising his hindquarters menacingly within striking distance—through the bottom of the trap—of my nose, as much as to say, "You know what's
coming next if you don't leave my mouth alone." So rather than
have the floor boards kicked completely out of the trap, I would
give him his head, which was all to the good.

One Christmas my late bungalow companion, who had been
transferred to another district, returned to join me in the local
festivities, and on Christmas Eve I carried him off in the buggy to
a dinner party eight miles away. Sitting behind the splendidly
stepping Mustard Pot for the first time he voted him at once a
rattling good trapper, but before he retired to bed next morning
he reversed his opinion. There were eight or nine of us present at
that party, and after doing full justice to the occasion, and ending

a very merry gathering in the early hours of a cold, raw and misty morning, we returned to our respective estates. On our journey home Mustard Pot became impatient; by the feel of his mouth I knew that his thoughts were centred on his long-delayed feed of oats, eight miles away. There was no holding him, but we were quite safe so long as he chose to remain in the middle of the road.

Somewhere along this jungle highway, and it was a highway in every respect, being raised eight feet above the surrounding flood level over most of its length, there was one of those deep, winding, stony, and, in the cold weather, quite dry river-beds. The bridge spanning this was out of commission, and a temporary diversion of precipitous and somewhat snaky proportions had been cut down the steep banks. On the outward drive in the early evening light, Mustard Pot, as was expected of him, had negotiated this obstacle with perfect skill and grace, and I checked and steered him carefully through and on to the road again.

On our homeward run there was a heavy white mist and we could see little farther than the points of Mustard Pot's ears, which were pricked at an angle that prophesied trouble. About half a mile from the bridge he was still in wonderful form. I thought it time we descended into low gear to allow the syce to get down and walk the horse and buggy through the cutting. Tactfully, with the reins, I began to explain the exigency of the occasion to Mustard Pot, but all my skill and soothing words of caution fell on deaf ears and a hard resisting mouth. I realised we were booked for instant trouble once we sighted the bridge-work, but refrained from upsetting my companion's unruffled calm.

"Fine gee, Mustard Pot," he had muttered some miles back. Since then he had been strangely silent, and I had almost forgotten he was there. The only hope of pulling the horse out of his long swinging stride in time was the doubtful use of force until he sickened of rebellion, but rough handling proved worse than futile. Instead of slackening his pace, he retaliated by breaking into a canter and beginning to kick. The more I attempted to

THE BRONCHO THAT WOULD NOT BE BROKEN

VACHEL LINDSAY

A little colt—broncho, loaned to the farm
To be broken in time without fury or harm,
Yet black crows flew past you, shouting alarm,
Calling "Beware," with lugubrious singing . . .
The butterflies there in the bush were romancing.
The smell of the grass caught your soul in a trance,
So why be a-fearing the spurs and the traces,
O broncho that would not be broken of dancing?

You were born with the pride of the lords great and olden
Who danced, through the ages, in corridors golden.
In all the wide farm-place the person most human.
You spoke out so plainly with squealing and capering,
With whinnying, snorting, contorting and prancing,
As you dodged your pursuers, looking askance,
With Greek-footed figures, and Parthenon paces,
O broncho that would not be broken of dancing.

The grasshoppers cheered. "Keep whirling," they said.
The insolent sparrows called from the shed
"If men will not laugh, make them wish they were dead."
But arch were your thought, all malice displacing,

Though the horse-killers came, with snake-whips advancing.
You bantered and cantered away your last chance.
And they scourged you; with Hell in their speech and their faces,
O broncho that would not be broken of dancing.

"Nobody cares for you," rattled the crows,
As you dragged the whole reaper next day down the rows.
The three mules held back, yet you danced on your toes.
You pulled like a racer, and kept the mules chasing.
You tangled the harness with bright eyes side-glancing,
While the drunk driver bled you—a pole for a lance—
And the giant mules bit at you—keeping their places.
O broncho that would not be broken of dancing.

In that last afternoon your boyish heart broke.
The hot wind came down like a sledge-hammer stroke.
The blood-sucking flies to a rare feast awoke.
And they searched out your wounds, your death-warrant tracing.
And the merciful men, their religion enhancing,
Stopped the red reaper to give you a chance.
Then you died on the prairie, and scorned all disgraces,
O broncho that would not be broken of dancing.

EQUESTRIAN INTERLUDE

TURSA

Roads in North-East India have been so widened and improved that cars and motor-cycles are largely replacing horses in the tea estates. Even in Darjeeling, where the narrow thoroughfares zigzag to a height of six thousand feet, there is a craze for running baby cars. But the planter still keeps his horses, cherished possession, for the rougher going in the rainy season, and for work that takes him far from the actual garden.

One of my first purchases on arrival up-country was a pony, bought from an elderly planter some miles away, who rather despised motoring, preferring the more delightful practice of driving in his smart buggy with three well-bred greys in line-ahead formation. The leader of this string of Australian walers was a mare called Jill, but it happened that one evening, while showing their best paces, Jill shied more violently than was prudent, and carried the other two greys, the buggy, and their redoubtable Jehu to the bottom of a deep khud. Their driver there and then concluded that Jill had become too great a handful for his advancing years, and, rather than risk breaking his neck, decided to sell her before any more damage was done, and content himself in future with driving a pair.

So I bought Jill remarkably cheap, and it was not long before I was aware that I had made a first-class bargain. She was rising seven at the time, and was still in my possession when she died ten years later: a grand, stout-hearted, flea-bitten waler mare, with magnificent points, a long streaming grey and white mane and tail, and standing fourteen two. Her only outstanding fault was a hard mouth, but after I had ridden her for some time and we began to understand each other's ways, the lady in her retained this particular piece of vice for others. In time I could do anything with Jill, controlling her entirely by leg and voice, and we became fast friends.

Every morning Jill was groomed at daybreak in the bungalow compound, just outside my open bedroom door, where, as the sun rose, I reclined in pyjamas drinking the early morning pot of fragrant tea and superintending the syce at his work. Her toilet completed, Jill would bear down upon the verandah, poke her head through the rails, and whinny for the stick of juicy sweet sugar-cane she knew lay hidden beneath my pillow. I was seldom without a stock of this tid-bit, and never forgot to give her a piece at the end of each day's outing. Were the reward not immediately forthcoming, Jill would follow me closely up the steps of the verandah, or impatiently paw the drive until she had had her way and the sugar-cane was produced.

On my daily ride to inspect the thousand-odd coolies employed on the various works on the estate, I could always dismount and leave Jill by herself to graze contentedly without the least fear of her taking to her heels and galloping off home. When my inspection was at an end a call to Jill from the far side of the labouring gang would make her pick her head up and trot over to where I waited. Having a contrary streak in her nature at times, like most members of her sex, she was addicted to fickleness, and more than once it was my lot to remember either the weight of her heels or the crunching nip of her teeth. But, of course, it was my own fault, for I delighted in teasing her. Sometimes she would suspect even my most innocent approach, and catching me off guard would scatter my daydreams with a pair of flying heels. Although I am sure she enjoyed being made a fuss of, she detested being tickled, and a playful pressure of the hand just behind the saddle always resulted in a first-class imitation of a bucking bronco.

She initiated me into the glorious game of polo, and we had many years on the field together. With me she played a perfect game, but when a stranger took her out for a chukker she never failed to shy off the ball at the moment of impact, pulling the whole time like a fiend, or she would take him completely off the field in one of her non-stop gallops. Her rider, after taking part in every evolution but that of striking the ball, was relieved when the gong sounded the end of the chukker.

The mare and I had many a painful spill together, but generally she managed to come off scot-free, or nearly so, and was polo-sound until the day she died. Not so I, who had some unlucky days. My teeth were smashed, collar bone broken, and a couple of cracked ribs once prevented me from laughing for two whole months. She was a game little lady, and many a cup I won with her. Besides polo, she jumped well, raced occasionally, and once we took the cup from a strong field over a reconnaissance course of twenty-two miles, through rice lands, river beds, scrub, and forest. I used her less strenuously as her years advanced, but she was an affectionate and bonny pony until the end, when she failed to come through an anaesthetic while in the hands of the vet. Stout-hearted old Jill.

Before that came Wilkie. He too was grey, a full-blooded 14.2 Arab, fast and handy on the polo field, but a terrible stumbling-block as a hack and lacking Jill's versatility. Although somewhat past his heyday Wilkie could certainly play polo, but since the greater part of his active life had been spent on the polo field, all he understood was a hand canter or a thundering gallop—I never knew him to trot. His legs were of little use to him anywhere but on grass as flat as a lawn, and in a couple of years they gave out altogether.

My next delve into the market produced the never-to-be-forgotten Mustard Pot, and with him Bush Girl, a couple of English-bred gees that had spent most of their life in India with the artillery. When the regiment left the country, the pick of their horses was disposed of, and as they were going remarkably cheap, there was an invasion of them into the tea districts, and I, among many others, decided to have a couple. They turned up trumps. Mustard Pot was a big raking chestnut gelding standing 15.3, and the mare, Bush Girl, at 14.3, promised, after some schooling, to develop into a first-class polo pony. She was just the handy size, short barrelled, quick off the mark, and with a mouth like silk.

Mustard Pot, owing principally to some of the nightmare drives he has given me, will always retain a lasting place in my memory. He was much too big and unwieldy for the polo field, but with the early schooling he had gone through with the artillery, he turned out to be a fast and capable trapper. To ensure that his abilities in this direction should not be wasted, or go to seed through want of practice, I hunted round and bought a second-hand buggy to keep him company. It was just as well that I had not gone in for a more expensive turnout, for the trap had not then been built that Mustard Pot could not have put the word 'finis' to when he felt inclined. He was a perfect, long-striding hack and untiring across country, taking bunds, ditches, and dykes in his fast and powerful stride without the least exertion. Pulling the light buggy was mere child's play to one who had been with the game.

A reliable horse at all other times, Mustard Pot had a rooted objection to late nights. Then he had to be handled with much circumspection and considerable skill. Even when being yoked into the buggy preparatory to the long homeward run, he was quite prepared to leave it standing, and it was an effort on the part of the syce and myself to get him between the shafts and hitched up at all. Seldom, if ever, did he give us time to settle comfortably into our seats. The syce stood at his head, both hands on the bit, while I collected the reins and held on to the trap. With a nimble jump to one side the syce would let go, and Mustard Pot, rising on his hind-legs with a mighty pull, would be off at once in top gear. In the meantime I had sprung dexterously towards the driving-seat; the syce, with a precision gained through much practice, would make a dive, for his perch at the rear as the buggy shot past him, and there would be no stopping Mustard Pot until he reached home.

There was never any check to his long raking trot through the mist and darkness; up-hill or down, the gradient meant little to him. With an easy feel of the mouth, I trusted in his road sense and my own lucky star, and mile after mile of jungle road dropped rapidly behind us. Mustard Pot, in his own powerful way, had much horse sense, and could always be relied upon to keep the middle of the road and take his corners wide, but never when in one of his 'get-a-move-on' moods would he tolerate a tightening or pulling of the reins. If he ever broke from his mile-eating trot to the canter, I was always to blame, and his night sight being far superior to my own, his mouth was generally left severely alone. As soon as I tried to ease or slow him up, he accepted the challenge, and fought me for the bit; and if I still persisted, he would arch his beautiful neck and break into a canter, raising his hindquarters menacingly within striking distance—through the bottom of the trap—of my nose, as much as to say, "You know what's coming next if you don't leave my mouth alone." So rather than have the floor boards kicked completely out of the trap, I would give him his head, which was all to the good.

One Christmas my late bungalow companion, who had been transferred to another district, returned to join me in the local festivities, and on Christmas Eve I carried him off in the buggy to a dinner party eight miles away. Sitting behind the splendidly stepping Mustard Pot for the first time he voted him at once a rattling good trapper, but before he retired to bed next morning he reversed his opinion. There were eight or nine of us present at that party, and after doing full justice to the occasion, and ending a very merry gathering in the early hours of a cold, raw and misty morning, we returned to our respective estates. On our journey home Mustard Pot became impatient; by the feel of his mouth I knew that his thoughts were centred on his long-delayed feed of oats, eight miles away. There was no holding him, but we were quite safe so long as he chose to remain in the middle of the road.

Somewhere along this jungle highway, and it was a highway in every respect, being raised eight feet above the surrounding flood level over most of its length, there was one of those deep, winding, stony, and, in the cold weather, quite dry river-beds. The bridge spanning this was out of commission, and a temporary diversion of precipitous and somewhat snaky proportions had been cut down the steep banks. On the outward drive in the early evening light, Mustard Pot, as was expected of him, had negotiated this obstacle with perfect skill and grace, and I checked and steered him carefully through and on to the road again.

On our homeward run there was a heavy white mist and we could see little farther than the points of Mustard Pot's ears, which were pricked at an angle that prophesied trouble. About half a mile from the bridge he was still in wonderful form. I thought it time we descended into low gear to allow the syce to get down and walk the horse and buggy through the cutting. Tactfully, with the reins, I began to explain the exigency of the occasion to Mustard Pot, but all my skill and soothing words of caution fell on deaf ears and a hard resisting mouth. I realised we were booked for instant trouble once we sighted the bridge-work, but refrained from upsetting my companion's unruffled calm.

"Fine gee, Mustard Pot," he had muttered some miles back. Since then he had been strangely silent, and I had almost forgotten he was there. The only hope of pulling the horse out of his long swinging stride in time was the doubtful use of force until he sickened of rebellion, but rough handling proved worse than futile. Instead of slackening his pace, he retaliated by breaking into a canter and beginning to kick. The more I attempted to

restrain him, the more vicious became his assaults on the bottom
of the trap, and in a very short time he had half the floor boards
splintered and littering the track. My friend ceased his deep breathing exercises and returned somewhat to his senses convinced that
it was an earthquake. I told him rather sharply to pull himself
together, because in a very few moments we should be leaving
the buggy.

I had no intention of continuing down the blind cutting with
Mustard Pot in his present frame of mind, and as clearly as possible I tried to drum this into my companion's bemused head, also
that the horse had more or less bolted; and that if I failed to master
him before reaching the river our best plan would be to roll over
the side of the buggy as compactly as possible. The barricade suddenly loomed up stark and threatening out of the mist ahead, and
as I managed with a great effort to steer the beast down the sharp
declivity to the right, I shouted lustily to my companion to jump,
dropped the reins, and quietly heaved myself over the splashboard
into the ditch.

I still think that he was under the impression that we had arrived home, that all he had to do was to step out of the buggy, and
that the violent jolting was just one of those purely internal affairs
of his own. At all events, instead of acting with the briskness the
occasion merited, he stood up unsteadily on the few remaining
floor boards and attempted to lower himself gently over the side,
his foot in search of the elusive foot-rest, which by this time was
not there. Failing to discover any foothold for his rocking form,
he suddenly disappeared from view beneath the wheels of the
racing buggy as it lurched drunkenly down the slope.

Freeing myself with some difficulty from the dense jungle of
the deep road-side drain that had broken my fall, I went in anxious
search of the buggy's other two occupants, muffled groans leading
me in the direction where at least one of them had fallen. There I
discovered my friend, who, judging by the noise he was making,
seemed to be in a very bad way, and I cursed myself, not forgetting

Mustard Pot, for running him into such a predicament. Apparently he had been run over by both wheels, one passing over his chest, bruising his ribs, while the other had taken one of his ankles, which appeared to be badly sprained. He was quite unable to walk, and after he had regained some of the breath that had been so unkindly knocked out of him, I left him sitting despondently in the mist and went off in search of some sort of conveyance to carry him home. Of the syce there was no trace, and I concluded he was either dead or already at home with Mustard Pot.

There were a few native huts in a clearing near-by, and after wakening the sleeping occupants and convincing them that I was human and not an apparition, I persuaded four of the men to accompany me, bringing one of their light string-beds to carry my injured friend the remaining three miles home. He refused to have anything further to do with buggies.

On the way home we discovered the syce sitting nursing his bruises beside what remained of the trap. Apparently he had clung to his oscillating perch until it had stopped, or, to be more exact, until that portion to which he belonged had come to a standstill; for Mustard Pot, finding himself in complete control, and kicking like a fiend to free himself, had gone on with the shafts. When we arrived home with our stretcher case a good hour afterwards, we discovered him patiently waiting to be admitted into his warm loose-box, and I was glad to find him none the worse.

That was not by any means the only time I had chosen the lesser of two evils by rolling out of the trap, but the horse had always managed to arrive with the empty buggy more or less intact.

Returning home once on one of these lonely drives through the darkness, with Mustard Pot behaving himself and going fast and well, and myself under the influence of a good dinner and good company, I became drowsy, and painfully returned to my sense by the roadside amidst a shower of sparks. It slowly dawned on me that my syce, who had also taken a purler, but a more gentle one than mine, was binding a puggri tightly round my head, and that my face was covered with blood. Swinging down an incline at our accustomed homing speed one of the wheels had struck half a tree-trunk that must have fallen from a passing cart that afternoon. Knowing the road to be in good repair, I had not been quite so wakeful as usual, and the impact had pitched me into a pile of rocks. Mustard Pot had gone on, naturally, leaving the syce and myself to walk the remaining miles through tiger and leopard in-fested jungle as best we could. I managed it without falling by the wayside, and, as usual, found the horse, still between the shafts, awaiting us and quietly demanding his evening ration of oats.

The doctor babu dressed and plastered up my wounds until the following morning, when the medico arrived and added to the general discomfort by stitching my head together again in several places, and counselling bed for three days' rest. Another piece of advice he quite unnecessarily tendered me was either to sell Mus-tard Pot or in future only use him as a hack, or one day I would undoubtedly break my neck. After one or two other occasions in which acrobatics played a leading part, and after seriously weigh-ing up the pros and cons of our career together, for I was very fond of the old beast, I reluctantly decided to pass him on to a friend of mine who needed a good hack, but only on the under-standing that he was never again placed between a pair of shafts. The old horse—he is an old horse now—is still doing his daily dozen round the work of the plantation; and if looks count for anything and one or two splints are ignored, there still remain a good many years of useful service ahead of him. But I hope he has long forgotten how to trap!

And so they came, stayed a while, and passed on. I had several others, some good, some indifferent, but never a bad one, and they were all stout friends.

Souvenir replaced Mustard Pot and taught me much about polo. He it was, too, who introduced me to the thrills of racing, and he won a number of cups for me over the shorter distances. I had him for eight years, and except when he once over-reached himself in a paper chase he was never sick or sorry—a great horse.

Racing led me into acquiring Billy, a hard-mouthed little Bhutan hill pony. A friend of mine joined in the venture and bought another of this same Himalayan breed. We trained Billy and Marquis together, and won several races.

The great difficulty was to keep them confined to the small and restricted circular tracks of the racecourse. A good deal of schooling and training was necessary, and it was no small part of the jockey's task to finish a race by passing the post, and not in an entirely different direction. We used to train our two little grey flyers in great secrecy for six weeks before the races were due to begin, as much to accustom the lightweight jockey to their short stride as to teach the ponies to gallop within the confines of the beflagged course. Since the various districts were cut off from each other by forest and rivers, we never knew the capabilities of the entries until the races took place, and we were always eager to spring a surprise on some of our rivals. We used to run our Bhutias against each other every day in the cool of the evening, over a measured course round the outskirts of our polo field, under conditions similar to those they would experience on the race-course. Each run was timed, and towards the end of their training we speeded them up into their best galloping form until the day of the races, when we knew that any other Bhutia that expected to leave them behind would have to move. We had to arrange for horse-boxes in advance and entrain our ponies; for these race meetings took place sixty miles away, and were always a great occasion with many shirts lost on the totalisator. Men backed their own club or district favourites, and anybody who could enter a 'dark horse' generally swept the pool.

Our two little Bhutias ran right well for us on every occasion, taking quite a load of rupees from the 'tote,' until they became so handicapped that to run them was too weighty an affair. When his racing days were over I rode Billy on the garden, eventually pensioning him off. He died peacefully of old age. Those of us who know the Indian bazaar horse-dealer know how much that meant.

THE BROWN MARE

ALFRED OLLIVANT

He used to bring her home when he came on his winter's leave in the years before the War, to hunt with the South Down; for she was an unusually fine performer across country. And it was there I met her.

A tall upstanding creature, sixteen hands and over, very high at the withers, not quite clean-bred and yet showing breeding in every line. She did not really carry bone enough for the heavy Wealden clay, in which your horse sinks up to his hocks at every stride; but the Major was clearly always pleased when the big iron-gray Granite had strained a sinew and he could fall back on the mare for an extra day. And little Humbleton, the very British groom, with the blue eyes, the chestnut hair, and stolid way, was just the same. When exercising, he always rode the mare for preference and led the gray. She was honest and she was kind, with the heart of a woman and the manners of a lady. Yet except for a general air of breeding I do not think you would have singled her out in a crowd.

Kitty came first into the Major's stable when after a long spell at the War Office he went back to regimental work and took over the command of Field Battery. I think he picked her out of the ranks; maybe the trumpeter had been riding her.

In that stable other horses came and went. The mare stayed; and her reputation grew.

At the big Aldershot meeting the Major entered her for the

Artillery Point-to-point. He was never hard on his horses, and didn't ride her out. She was not placed. Afterwards he heard the whole Brigade had been backing her.

When the Major got his Jacket and took command of the Black Horse Battery at the Wood, Humbleton and the mare went with him. She was not black: she was brown. Therefore he could not ride her on ceremonial parades as his first charger. So he bought a sporting little black horse with a short back, Dandy by name, on which he rode with nodding plume at the head of his Troop down Park Lane, across Piccadilly and the Mall, to fire salutes on Horse Guards Parade.

But if she was no longer his first charger she was still first in his heart; and for long days on Salisbury Plain during autumn manoeuvres she had not her equal.

There followed three quiet years of preparation, the Black Horse Battery doing the Musical Drive at Olympia, swirling at the gallop in rhythmic figures interlaced about the famous bronze Gundamuck gun which the Troop had lost when covering the retreat from Cabul in the first Afghan War and recovered forty years later in the second. The Battery drove to the admiration of connoisseurs, artists, and the London crowd; and then would march down to Salisbury Plain to break records there in the mimic business of war.

Then came the reality; and the Major had to make the sacrifice of his life, and break up in a moment the fighting unit which through three laborious years he had trained to the point of perfection. Immediately on mobilization he was called upon to send all his horses, all his men, and half his officers to complete the strength of a first-for-service Battery at Aldershot. He stood with folded arms on the barrack-square and watched the famous black teams, shining in the sun and beloved of Londoners, file out of the gate. The subalterns said they thought the Major's heart would break. It was perhaps a little comfort to him that when horses and men arrived at Aldershot the Major of the first-for-service Battery there asked his own gun-team drivers to give place to the new-comers.

"These are the drivers of the Black Horse Troop," he said.

The only men left the Major were Humbleton and his batman; the only horses Dandy and the mare. For the rest he had his guns; his non-commissioned officers; a couple of subalterns, reservists, and the pick of all the horses that were streaming into London with which to build up a new Battery.

II

He had two months in which to do it; and he did it.

In those days there was no tarrying. The Germans were knocking at the Gates of Calais.

At the beginning of October the Black Horse Battery, its horses no longer black, many-coloured, many-cornered, but a hard and handy crowd, disembarked at Zeebrugge with the Seventh Division in the romantic and desperate endeavour to relieve Antwerp; and the officers of the Guards Brigade to which the Battery was attached muttered among themselves that if it was no longer the Battery of Olympia days it was still the best Horse Battery in England.

Antwerp fell the day they landed. The Immortal Division, 20,000 strong, marched out to meet the enemy much as David went to meet Goliath. In a perilously thin-drawn-out line it flung itself across the path of the German herds driving bull-headed, hundred thousands of them, for the sea and the island that lay across the Channel.

General French sent word to the valiant Division that he would reinforce them in five hours. Those reinforcements took five days to come. But the Division held; though at the end of the stress it had but forty officers left out of the four hundred who had disembarked at Zeebrugge six weeks before.

In those tremendous days Black Horse Battery played its fiery part in support of the First Battalion of the Grenadier Guards.

Tried in that white-hot furnace, Guardsmen and gunners proved worthy of each other and of the traditions of their great regiments. There was no rest by night or day for officers, men, or horses.

Kitty, the mare, took it all very calmly. Back with the limbers, on the sheltered side of the ridge on which the guns were barking, she stretched her long neck, bowed a knee, and grazed the Flemish turf at ease much as on Salisbury Plain. The hubbub across the ridge, her master's fierce peremptory voice, the occasional burst of shrapnel near by, disturbed her little.

Now and then the trumpeter, handing over the mare and his own horse to the care of Humbleton, would crawl to the top of the ridge and watch the Battery in action beyond, pounding away at the greycoats struggling in the valley. He didn't see much: for the guns were roughly dug in. But once he saw a farmhouse which the Major was using for observation post crash down in headlong ruin.

"Gosh!" muttered the trumpeter. "Spotted 'im. He's done."

Then the long, lean Major came running out of the dust and debris.

The trumpeter returned at the trot to his horses.

"Old man ain't 'alf nippy," he reported to Humbleton.

"He ain't so old neether, then," answered Humbleton, who took no liberties with his master himself, and allowed none.

"Ain't he, then," retorted the trumpeter who must have the last word even in the mouth of Hell. "I'll lay he's older than he were twenty year ago, then."

Once on that last desperate day, when the one skeleton Cavalry Brigade held in reserve was dashing here and there to make good as best it might gaps in the broken line, the Major got his guns up under a wall to cover the Guards' counter-attack launched as a forlorn hope. The Germans saw him and swept the wall away with a tidal wave of fire.

It was *Rear limber up!* and the gun-teams came up at the gallop.

In the hubbub and tumult of shells, shouts, of gunners furiously handling gun-wheels, of drivers with outstretched whip-hands quieting their teams, of bloody men disengaging bloody and floundering horses, Kitty, the mare, was steady as a rock.

"Got her, sir?" gasped the trumpeter, as he toppled off his own horse.

"Right," said the Major, toe in his stirrup, and swung into his saddle. *"Battery column, gallop!"*

And somehow or other the Battery swung clear.

Those were astounding days. For three weeks the officers and men of that Battery never had their clothes off, and for days together the horses were never unharnessed. But whoever else went short Kitty, the mare, never suffered. Humbleton saw to that, and to be just the mare saw to herself in her large and sensible way, grazing when opportunity offered, and snatching *bonne bouches* from ruined haystacks.

After the first terrible six weeks the Armies settled down to trench warfare. It was not the game for Horse Artillery; but the Black Horse Battery played it with zest all through that first winter.

The horses stood out in the open and thrived. Kitty grew a coat like a bear's; and the saddle sank into her back as into a drift of brown snow. But campaigning suited her as it did her black companion Dandy.

Then came promotion.

The Major, now a Brevet-Lieutenant-Colonel, took command of a Field Artillery Brigade. That did not last for long. Within a few weeks he and Humbleton and the two horses were back with the Horse Artillery, the Colonel now commanding a Brigade.

III

The Headquarters of the Brigade was in a chateau some thirty miles behind the firing line.

When the turn of the Cavalry Division, to which the Brigade

was attached, came for a spell in the trenches, horses and guns made a long forced march by night and took up their positions early in December of the second winter of the War.

They had three months in the trenches—months of sleet and rain, of dogged endurance, infinitely dull, varied by lurid nightmare interludes.

When towards the end of February they were relieved nobody in the Division regretted it.

That was the time of the heavy snows; and all reliefs were made of necessity at night.

The Horse Artillery started for the thirty-mile trek home at midnight, the long thin line of guns, their wheels thick with snow, trailing worm-like through the white dimness that muffled the noise of their going and made the procession strangely ghost-like.

Wagons and kits were to follow later.

The Colonel gave his Brigade an hour's start.

It was just one when his batman came to the door of his much-shelled lodging and announced that Humbleton and the horses were outside.

The Colonel, busy destroying papers, went to the door, accompanied by his terrier Bruiser. The little groom, in his goat-skin coat, stood outside in the snow, the horses in hand. Dandy stretched a neck to greet his little friend, the terrier, standing three-legged, and shivering in the snow, while the mare nibbled tentatively at a pile of wood close by.

"Don't let her eat that!" ordered the Colonel ferociously.

He always spoke to his servants as if they were his mortal enemies and he wished them to know he knew it. And they took more from him than they would have done from many a man with a smoother tongue and a smaller heart. It was just the old man's way, they said among themselves. And he had the qualities which ensured respect if they did not win love. He was just, consistent, and in the heart of him considerate. So, to the surprise of many, they always stuck to him.

The Colonel went back to his room with Bruiser, and piled on layer upon layer of clothes: sweaters, hunting-waistcoats, Norfolk jackets, towards the top a suit of oilskins, and over all a Burberry.

In multitudinous pockets he stuffed an electric torch, a flask, a thermos, a map, a ball of string, an extra pair of gloves, a muffler, and other odds and ends. The lean Colonel, now a very portly man, gave certain curt instructions to his batman, tied Bruiser, who was to follow with the kits, to the leg of the table, and mounted Dandy: for he knew of old that the mare was not clever in the snow.

Then he set off into the night, Humbleton and the mare following in his wake.

Once clear of the village the Colonel looked round. In that little distance he had already gained greatly on the other pair.

He waved for the groom to come up alongside.

"Leg her up," he ordered gruffly. "Keep her alongside me."

Side by side master and man rode along through the night, the snow coating them heavily.

"She's walking abominably," said the Colonel.

"Yes, sir," answered Humbleton, who never wasted words, least of all on his master.

Laboriously the Colonel disengaged his electric torch and flashed it on the mare.

What he saw he didn't like.

The snow was heavy on her shoulders, thick in her ears, plastering her heavy coat; and she was slouching along disconsolately, her head down, as though smelling out a track.

It's that wood poisoned her, thought the Colonel; but he didn't say anything.

"Does she feel all right?" he asked.

"Yes, sir," answered Humbleton.

Twelve miles out they stopped at a little *estaminet* for a water and feed.

Dandy tucked into his nose-bag greedily. The mare would not look at hers.

"Come on, missus," said Humbleton.

He warmed some water, making a weak gruel, sprinkled bran on the top, and held the bucket to her nostrils temptingly.

She breathed on it, her breath mingling with the steam, but would not touch it.

The Colonel walked round her with anxious eyes, pulled her ears, hand-rubbed her cold pasterns.

It's that wood, he thought.

Then he rummaged in his multitudinous pockets. After long search he produced a thermometer and took her temperature.

It was 103, and there was still a twenty-mile march before them.

He got her a ball and gave it her.

There was no stabling at the *estaminet;* and nothing for it therefore but to go on.

He swung into his saddle again.

The track lay before them invisible save for the half-obliterated furrows left by the gun-wheels. The snow came waving across them in white curtains that almost seemed to lighten the darkness. The moustaches of both men froze and were thatched with snow. The two white-cloaked figures laboured along side by side like two phantom horsemen with feet of lead.

The mare seemed to come on a little better.

Every now and then the Colonel said—

"How's she feel now?"

And Humbleton answered—

"Very queer, sir."

At length they came to the foot of a long bare ridge, stretching interminably before them, smooth and bleak and white as a shroud, great curtains of snow flapping dismally across its desolate face.

The mare stopped.

Both men dismounted. The Colonel with a hoof-picker, disengaged with difficulty from a remote interior pocket, emptied her hoofs of the balling snow.

He thought she was going to lie down; and once she lay down on that slope he knew he would never get her up again.

He and Humbleton, crouching in the snow, hand-rubbed her legs and flanks. Then they started leading her up the slope.

The two men were wonderfully kind and patient with the suffering creature; far more kind and patient with her than with each other.

The forlorn little group toiled desolately up the slope, now engulfed in a billow of waving white, now emerging into blotted dimness, the wind rollicking away with terrible laughter in the valley below. The horses, with windy tails tucked-in and strewn about their flanks, plodded on with downward heads, shaking the snow from their ears like big dogs with a rattle of accoutrements that sounded weirdly in the night.

Honest and kind as always, the mare was doing her dumb best; and both men knew it. One on either side, they shouldered her up the slope, easing her, halting her, talking to her, coaxing her on a step at a time, as a nurse teaching a child to walk. And every now and then she rubbed her snowy head against one man or the other, as though recognizing their love, and wishing to tell them about it.

Somehow or other they bolstered her up to the top of that Ridge of Windy Death.

Down in the valley, on the other side, the Colonel hoped he might find a Cavalry Division, and some shelter for the mare.

He was right.

As they descended the slope, the mare walking more easily, they found themselves among friends.

The Gunners were in possession of the valley.

Officers and men with lanterns came to the rescue. Most of them knew the Colonel; many of them the mare. A veterinary surgeon was found and pulled out of his bed. The mare was given a roomy box in a farm. She revived somewhat. Willing hands bedded her down in bracken. Humbleton set to work to warm and dry her. The Colonel took her temperature and found it less.

The light was just stealing over the white-bosomed hills and snow-thatched roofs when he swung into the saddle to ride the last long stage to his Headquarters alone.

The mare was playing with some hay, and Humbleton was rugging her up, as he left her.

IV

All that day he was busy, and no news came through; but a horse of his Orderly Officer died partly from exposure and partly from eating wood, the vet. said.

Next morning early the Colonel rode off to the valley where the mare was to see how things were going.

As he rode up to the yard of the farm, Humbleton, looking in his goat-skin like a little clean-shaven Robinson Crusoe, came ploughing through the snow to meet him.

He looked very dogged and did not catch the Colonel's eye.

"Well?" said the Colonel.

"Mare's dead, sir," answered the little man.

"Indeed!" said the Colonel rudely. "What time?"

"Two o'clock this morning."

The Colonel said nothing and dismounted.

Heavily he walked through the slush of the farmyard towards the loose-box and entered.

Honest and kind in death as in life, the brown mare lay on her side, rough of coat, her long neck stretched out, her long flat thin legs slightly crooked, her shoes upturned and shining, looking strangely pathetic.

Over head Humbleton had scrawled in chalk upon a beam:

Kitty:
Died for her country
1 *March*, 1916

The Colonel stood above her.

He was glad she had such a thick bed of bracken to rest upon. Then he bent and felt her heart.

One of those strange and overwhelming waves of emotion, of which we cannot trace the origin, came surging up out of the inland ocean of his being and choked him.

He kicked the bracken about with his feet, and blew his nose. Then he said—

"We shall miss her, Humbleton."

The little groom, standing in his goat-skin jacket in the door, his back towards his master, looked out over the snow and answered nothing.

"JOKER"

(A Horse That Lived Up to His Name)

WILL JAMES

Joker had already been named such before he was turned over to me, and a joker he sure turned out to be. For a horse he could get himself into more predicaments that would wind up into jokes on himself, including his rider, than most humans do.

He was a young horse, had been rode only a few times when I slipped my rope on him and went to work for the desert cow outfit he belonged to. I'd hired out to ride for that outfit and, as the joker horse he was, he fooled me the first time I laid eyes on him.

The foreman was in the corral with me, pointing out the string of horses another rider had started breaking and I was to finish. Joker was one of 'em, a mighty well set up and good size blood bay, and running and snorting around the way he was, drawed my attention to him more than did the others.

Being a stranger in that country and wanting to make a sort of acquainting conversation with the foreman I asked him how much that Joker horse would weigh. He answered: "Make a guess."

It might be hard for some to believe but in some of the range countries, sometimes only a hundred miles or so separating, a horse of the same size and appearance will vary from one to two hundred pounds in weight, sometimes more. That's due to the kind of feed different ranges produce, also climate. Many an experienced horse dealer is fooled by the weight of a horse on that account, also by their age, for a horse from sandy, dry and brushy ranges will show a younger mouth than the one from the tall grass ranges and where running water is a-plenty.

As I've already said, Joker was a well set up and good sized horse and I made my guess according to the many such size and built horses I'd handled on other ranges. After I'd caught and walked up to him I guessed him to weigh eleven hundred.

The foreman grinned some. "I weighed him at the stockyards just a few days ago," he says, "and with saddle and all he weighed nine hundred and twenty."

Well, that was one at my expense from Joker.

It was on the next day when one of Joker's jokes turned on him. I'd made all ready the day before to hit out with a string of eight broncs, with only one gentle horse for pack and snubbing. The foreman had left me alone at the desert cow camp, figuring on making another such camp across a stretch of thirty miles and no water between (no distance for an automobile but no such country where an automobile could move).

To be sure of making that distance, along with driving my string of broncs, I picked on one in the string which I figured would have the age, and be hard and tough enough to stand up under the long and dry ride.

After the job of saddling and topping this horse, making it as I could so's to save him and myself, I opened the corral gate to start out with my string, the only gate from there to the camp I was headed for.

My string came out of the corral quiet enough, and then, a short distance down a dry wash, and all going well, this Joker horse of a sudden broke loose and like a bullet hit straight out for the horse range, where I'd got him from with the others just the day before.

There was no chance of heading him off. I tried but the horse I was riding "bogged" his head (went to bucking) and then stampeded another direction, no stopping him.

After finally circling him towards where my string had been, they'd also started, and going another direction from where I wanted 'em to go. With my horse now some winded, I manoeuvred him so's to turn 'em. As good luck would have it, they'd stayed together, Joker being the only one missing and now very much out of sight. I had to let him go, figuring I would get him a month or so later, when I'd get back to the main camp again.

But such wasn't to be, not according to Joker, and along about the heat of noon that same day there come a streak of dust, and a blood bay horse making it. It was Joker. He'd made a circle of the horse range, looking for a bunch he was used to running with, and not finding it, had returned to the string, for there was two in the string that had belonged to the same bunch.

Joker had made quite a circle and covered more than a few miles by then, and he was good to stay with the string, behaving well until camp was reached. His wild break away had turned out to be a wild goose chase and a sort of joke. To his expense this time.

Another joke at his expense was when the foreman of this same outfit rode up to my camp and said that the owner (a mining man who knew a lot about ore and holes in the ground but nothing about cattle) ordered him to have me move to another spring camp and run in what he thought was a weak cow he'd drove by and seen standing in the middle of a big dry and high mesa flat, with a calf by her side, dying of thirst, he thought, and starving.

I was having my hands full with quite a few hundred head of mighty scattered cattle at the time, and the mention of having me move to another camp to take care of just one lone cow and calf, more than made me and the foreman wonder and laugh some.

But orders was orders, and I sure didn't mind such an order because I'd been riding mighty hard for some time. Another rider took my place and my string, all but Joker. I figured he'd be just the horse I'd need for that lone and easy job, for, with his funny and tricky ways he'd sort of keep me company.

The time being winter and no stock running in that higher country, the owner had some grub and baled hay freighted some fifty miles in to the camp for just me, Joker and cow and calf. That and my time alone cost more than the cow was worth but that wasn't considered, nor any of my business, and right then I figured I'd have some easy riding for some days, at least until the owner of the outfit found out that all the cow needed was a good shove down country where she belonged.

The first day of my expected easy riding didn't start so good —I found the cow. She wasn't exactly in prime shape for beef. If she had been she'd been easier to handle, and as she was, she was just in good shape to fight, and her husky calf was right aching for a good run.

The cow was pretty wild, and being alone with her calf that way, and the sight of a rider coming up on her, done everything but make her any tamer. I seen right away I'd have trouble getting that old heifer to the corral where I was to feed her, and I took her as easy as possible, staying a good distance away and not turning her any more often than I could help, for, by her actions she just wanted an excuse to get on the fight, and one turn or two too many would be sure to set her off.

I let her amble on pretty well as she pleased for a ways, and being I'd started her right, she headed on near the direction of the corral, only kind of at an angle. I let her amble on that direction for a ways, figuring on turning her when reaching the head of a dry wash which started from the mesa, wound thru the jack pine and led on down to near where the corral was.

Spooky cattle often take to down country well, especially a wash, and if the rider sort of keeps out of sight they'll sure ramble on in trying to lose him and not try to "brush" on him.

Joker was working good, and when the right time come I spurted him onto her so sudden that she just like sort of fell off the rim and into the head of the wash without looking where she was going or hesitating to want to fight, and down country she went, hers and her calf's tails a-popping.

All was going fine and I kept my distance. But the fun wasn't over yet. It hadn't even started, for getting the both in the delapidated corral that was down some miles and at the edge of the wash, would still be the hardest to do. The short wings of the corral was about as good as none, and to make it still more ticklish there was some inches to a foot coating of ice at the only gate, all over the corral and down past it a ways. That ice had formed from a spring above it, and that camp and corral seldom being used, the run of the water from it took its own course.

There was a small shed at one side of the corral where the supposed-to-be poor cow and calf was to be put and it was up to me to put 'em there.

Being I hadn't crowded the cow none while she and her calf hightailed down the wash, only to get a glimpse of 'em once in a while and see that they was going right, they was sort of calmed down some when she reached the place to where I was to turn 'em towards the corral.

The cow turned easy enough and went on peaceful, until she came to the corral and the ice, and then, as I'd expected, her calf of a sudden broke away and the cow also whirled to make a dash for a break. Expecting that, I of course had my loop ready. I had her too close now to let her get away. I piled it onto her as she tried to run past, at the same time put Joker to speed on thru the corral gate, forgetting about the coating of ice and his getting any footing there. But with the speed we went there was no stopping, and being there was quite a slope inside the corral there was nothing for the cow to do but swap ends and follow. The shed was at the lower end of the corral. The cow, now on the fight, even tho she was sliding down on her side piled up in the shed, right with me and Joker, all on our sides.

There was a crash, bang against the log wall of the shed as the three of us hit it all in one heap. With watching the cow's horns and the slack of my rope so I wouldn't get tangled up in it, I was pretty busy, and so was Joker, for he didn't want to be in such close quarters with that mad cow and her horns. When we all crashed into the log wall, there was enough impact so that it broke some and Joker went on halfways thru. He done the rest in getting all the way thru.

He'd got his footing from the falling logs, bark and all there was under the shed, and left me there with the cow. I didn't want her to go thru the same hole we made, so, I dodged her horns and tied her down before she could get up, with the same rope I'd caught her with and forgot it was still hard and fast to the saddle horn.

Joker no more than got out of the shed when on slick ice he again lost his footing and slid on his side plum to the end of the rope, drawing it tight, and now he couldn't get his feet under him so as to get up. So there he was on the outside and down, and the cow inside also down.

I had a hard time standing up myself as I went along the rope to him, and the rope being so tight I seen where the only way he could get up was to uncinch the saddle and let him slide away from it to where he could get his footing.

He looked kind of foolish after that was done and finally got to his feet again. But the only joke there was on him that time was how he sure wasn't going to bed down with that mad cow crowding him so close, and then afterwards hitting the end of the rope and get "busted" (thrown) so he couldn't get up.

Both cow and horse now taken care of, I made an opening in a bare part of the corral and didn't have too much trouble getting the calf in. But I was sure to change the course of that spring water right afterwards. The ice soon got soft then and in a couple of days the most of it had melted away, leaving the corral more fit to use again.

It was in that same corral some days later when Joker, acting funny, took another bust. For having nothing to do as it was, with all the good hay he could eat, he got to feeling more rollicky than ever, if that was possible, for he always was full of the old nick plenty of snorts.

This time I was going to catch him, figuring to ride to another spring, more to pass the time away than thinking there'd be any stock there that would need attention. I tried to stop him so I could walk up to him but there was no chance there. I made a few tries, and seeing there was nothing doing that way I went and got my rope.

Feeling as good as he did, the sight of my rope with ready loop, acted sort of like a fuse in the dynamite that was in him, and before I could get within throwing distance of him he just sort of bounced, like a spooked antelope, and hit for the delapidated but tall corral gate— He hit it plum center and high, but not clearing it, and with the force and speed he hit it the gate crashed to splinters. At the same time, his knees caught on the top pole which up-ended him to land quite a ways and to a mighty hard fall.

It all happened so quick that all I done was stand in the corral with sudden thought that there I was without a horse, afoot, for, knowing his tricks as I did, I figured he'd jump right up and high-tail it down country. There was only one fence in that part of the desert country and that was the corral fence, then it was all open (and still is) till the next corral miles away was reached, no pastures.

But to my surprise, when Joker jumped up, looked around kind of dazed and then spotted me inside the corral, he bowed his neck and jumped right back over the gate he'd splintered just a few seconds before, and into the corral again, shook his head, and snorting, stopped to within a few feet of me, facing and watching. He'd thought me responsible for the fall he'd just had, and that he'd get another if he tried to break away from me again.

Where he'd got that education was that, along with other happenings we'd had, and the one of just a few days before where he'd took such a slide and hard fall, he'd come to thinking he'd only get the worst of it by trying to break away. He stood quivering, but plum still then as I walked up to him and slipped my rope over his head.

I was at that camp about a week when I took it onto myself to turn that cow and calf out and shove 'em to a country where they belonged. Where they ought to've been in the first place. Then I rode on to the main camp where I took on a fresh string of horses and went to riding from other spring camps, where a rider was really needed.

But I kept Joker in with the new string, and I was riding him along one day when I run onto a lanky steer with one horn grown bent and which was gouging into his upper jaw. That steer had been missed in quite a few round-ups or that horn would have been taken care of.

I soon seen why he'd been missed, for he run alone, and soon as he seen me he was gone like a deer, hitting for a thick patch of that brushy country. But this time he was some distance too far away from it, and before he could get to it my loop caught up with him.

But not as I wanted it to, for instead of catching him by his one straight horn and the head as I intended, the loop sailed down alongside his nose and caught him by one front foot. I didn't know I'd caught him until I pulled up on my slack, and then things happened.

It was an accident and one of the queer ones that happens with roping, but at the speed we all was going down the steep side hill, and I pulling up my slack, that steer upended to a clean turn over. He upended a second time and then as he got to scrambling to his feet, all with no let up in the speed, and neither Joker nor me expecting any such, Joker run right onto that steer's upraised rump, turning him over once more, and as that steer turned over again, Joker and me was also very much upraised by his frame, like from a prop that of a sudden come up, and at the speed we was going we was raised high and to sail on quite a ways before landing.

It was a hard landing, amongst rocks and many kinds of prickly brush. But Joker took the hardest fall, 'cause I know we went to the end of the rope before we got back to earth again. Joker got the sudden jerk of the tied rope which flipped him to land harder. As for me I just went sailing on, to roll over a few times and stop against a nice big boulder.

I looked back to see Joker up, all spooky from the fall. The steer was still down, with his head under him, and I tried to get at Joker before he went to the end of the rope again. But one glance of where it was and I knew what would happen. It happened during that one glance, for, as Joker got to his feet the rope was between his hind legs. As goosy as he always was, especially right then, and as he felt that rope between his hind legs, was all that was needed to stir things some more. He hunched up, made a high buck jump against it and he near fell again, but this time the rope broke near the loop end, snapped back and popped him on the rump—and Joker went from there.

As I seen him go I figured sure I was afoot this time, and so far from camp I didn't dare think about it. I didn't for the time anyway, 'cause the steer drawed my attention. He was now up, wild-eyed and looking around, aching to fight anything that moved and run to get at it. I edged to the big boulder on all fours, and as he spotted me it sure didn't take me no time to scramble up on top of it. I felt the breeze of him as he went by and thought sure he'd take a wing off my chaps with his one good horn as I scrambled up.

He didn't go but a few yards when he turned, and seeing me on top of that boulder I thought sure he'd tackle it. I wish he had and I done everything but try to stop him from doing it. But that steer had seen and dodged plenty of boulders before, and shaking his head, like daring me to be fool enough to come down off of it, he blowed on past it again and on he went for the thick and thorny brush where he'd first headed for when my rope upended him. And as he went on that way shaking his head at every shadow as he went, still looking for something to fight, I noticed that one bum horn of his, which had been growing in his jaw, had been broken off in the tumble. The work I wanted to do was done, and like yanking off a bad tooth and more, he'd now soon be all right.

I watched him go, and knowing he wouldn't return for some time I climbed down from the boulder and started on the way Joker had stampeded, not with any thought of ever finding or catching up with him, only he'd gone the direction of camp, the closest water, and a good many miles away. All I thought of was they'd sure be long ones.

I took off my chaps, throwed 'em over my back to keep the sun off, also not to hinder my walking, and as I started it was in no running walk but one set to last for some long distance, and to make it.

It was one of the very few times in my life I'd ever been set afoot. The ones before had been where I'd have to make just a few strides, and it looked like this time would sure make up for them, also any others that might come later on.

Being so all set to make the distance, I was near disappointed when going around a ledge, and not over half mile from where the steer had been well stopped, I seen Joker a-standing there and like he was petrified.

I stood sort of petrified too, and wondering what the samhill could have stopped and was holding him. I didn't stand petrified long, and at the sight of him my disappointment soon went the opposite as I unlimbered myself towards him.

He seen me at about the same time I did him, and he didn't budge. His head was the wrong way from where he'd started. He'd turned around and seemed fixed at watching something on the ground in front of him.

I eased up then, and near had to laugh as I came near and seen what he'd been watching and seemed to hold him. It was the broken end of the rope which had got between his legs during the fall and snapped at him as he'd got up and stampeded. In his running the rope had whipped to one side and he'd turned to face it, afraid to move, for fear of getting another fall and pop on the rump.

Thinking it might spook him to another start I didn't pick up the end of the rope as I came near him. Instead I just took hold of the bridle reins, then the rope, and I never seen such a show of relaxing as I did on that horse after I had coiled up what was left of that rope and hung it safe up on the saddle and out of his way.

That was another joke on Joker, for, even tho it wouldn't of done him no good at the end of the long run, he could easy kept on going. Many good and well broke rope horses would have, but I was mighty glad Joker had got to thinking he'd better not.

Joker played many jokes on himself and his rider that way, seldom with his knowing or meaning to. He was all life and go, and played jokes when free and among other horses. He was a born joker.

CHAMPIONS OF THE PEAKS

PAUL ANNIXTER

Slippy himself was primarily to blame for what happened that fall day. He had always been a bit too independent for his own good, and since his friendship with old Sounder, the ranch dog, had sprung up, he'd been a constant worry to Jesse Hunnicutt.

Slipstream, he was called—Slippy for short—and he'd been named for his speed. His hide was the color of running bronze. When in action with flying mane and wild of eye and nostril, his head might have been that of Pegasus the winged. He was only a two-year-old, but already the pride of High Ranch. Some day, Jesse Hunnicutt believed, Slippy would be as good as any of the champion polo ponies he had raised.

There was nothing really bad about Slippy. He was just full of ideas and pranks which walled him off from serious training. Sometimes in his wide-browed skull a cunning brain seemed bent on mischief—at least, so Jake Marden, the ranch foreman, claimed. Let a day dawn when a visiting buyer was to appear and Slippy would disappear up the mountain. As High Ranch was fenceless open range there was little to be done about this, unless someone remembered to lock Slippy in the barn.

It was old Sounder who had really gotten Slippy into the habit of these disappearances. He was the special property of young Jesse, who was fifteen, and old Jesse's only son. Part Walker, with an admixture of mastiff in his blood, Sounder had a seamed and melancholy face, big bones, great lubberly paws, and the heart of a lion. No respecter of bounds or barriers was Sounder, but a privileged character who spent a great share of his days on the heights, tracking rabbit, fox, or wild cat.

Slippy had met Sounder one day in spring far up among the piñon pines. They had smelled noses and each had belonged specially to the other from there on in. They had met often after that, up there in the peaks, far from the sounds and scents of the ranch. Sometimes the pair would remain away for two days and two nights running, dependent upon one another for company and moral support; Slippy feeding and rolling in some cup between the peaks where the grass grew lush all summer, Sounder digging for marmots on a near-by slope or tracking rabbits in the brush, till darkness brought them close together. Great days for them both.

Alone, Slippy would never have had the initiative for such forays, but with Sounder to lead the way, the long wanderings among the crags were an endless adventure. At such times, with all the animals' wild instincts uppermost, not even young Jesse or old Jesse himself could get near the two when they happened to sight them among the peaks.

So it was on the November day in question. For some time knife-edged blasts of wind had warned of bad weather close at hand, but Jesse Hunnicutt had elected to stay at High Ranch till snow actually fell. Then one morning the ranch hands awoke at dawn with a norther sobbing through the cracks and chinks of the bunkhouse and a sting of sleet in the air. Dun clouds hung low over the peaks and the valleys were lost in a smudgy haze. There was not an hour to spare if they expected to get stock and equipment to the lowlands in time to escape the oncoming blizzard.

Slippy and Sounder were missing again. Both had been away overnight, and old Jesse muttered profanely as he scanned the high trails. Within an hour gear and stock were ready to move, and still no sign of the runaways. Grudgingly Jesse gave the order to leave, but he himself rode up-trail a way for one last look for

Slipstream. Young Jesse followed on Uncle, a solid, sure-footed piebald.

For nearly an hour the two searched and called into the teeth of the wind, but to no avail. Slippy and Sounder were far up the mountain at the time, taking refuge in the lee of a rock ledge. Old Jesse hated to abandon the search, not the least of his reasons being the loss of one of the most promising horses ever raised on High Ranch. For when he turned his mount down-trail that day he never expected to see Slipstream alive again, though he hid the fact from his son.

"We'll come back when the weather breaks and look for them again, son," he placated. "Old Sounder'll come through, never fear. But we've got to go now, or we'll never get down the mountain."

When the storm broke shortly before dawn, Slipstream was sheltered in a high spruce grove where he had spent a chilly and restless night. Sounder was afar, engaged in his endless game of digging out mountain marmots, and now and then coursing after snowshoe rabbits. Slippy could hear him from time to time, sounding his hoarse bell-like hunting cry.

By the time the sleet had turned to driving snow, Sounder gave up his splendid game and sought his friend among the trees. When morning came with the storm increasing, uneasiness began to ride the pair. What feeding there was had already been covered with snow. Slippy's thoughts turned to the warmth and security of the great barns at High Ranch. He had had enough for a time of this fodderless freedom. So, too, had Sounder. But when their steps turned down-trail and they emerged from the shelter of the spruce, they were almost swept from their feet by the sheer force of the gale. In places the snow was already belly-deep on Sounder, and everything familiar about the landscape had been obliterated.

Sounder and Slipstream pressed on, heads bent to the blast. Trails were gone. Only their sure feet and their wild instincts kept them to the right way. On the steep slopes they slipped and scrambled precariously, then picked a slow and dextrous course along a mile of shelving rock ledges that pinched off into space. Later it was an even greater battle bucking through the drifts of the sheltered places.

It was far past midday when they sighted the ranch buildings and Slippy experienced one of his first great shocks. The ranch was deserted. Not a trace of smoke rose from the ranch-house chimneys, and there were not even any fresh tracks to show which way the men had gone.

Behind the summer lean-to the two took refuge and there Slippy found a few wisps of hay and straw in the long feed trough. Still others he uncovered by pawing the snowy ground beneath. Somewhat heartened by these mementos of man he settled down, eyes half closed, sensitive ears a-twitch, to await the ranchers' return. But Sounder had no such illusions. He prowled forlornly, whining with a growing unrest.

All that day the storm continued. Slippy finished every last sprig of hay in the lean-to. As the darkness of another night descended on the mountain wilderness, he lifted his voice in sharp, imperative neighs. But no one came.

Through the dark hours the two runaways huddled together for warmth. When another day dawned with no lessening of the storm, loneliness and growing fear gripped Slippy. All that day the two waited and shivered in a world filled with storm, cold, and misery. But no one came, and through a second stormy night they pressed together for very life's sake, their coats covered with a thickening layer of frost and snow.

By noon of the third day the storm had subsided. Sounder set off down the mountain, whither he knew the ranch hands had gone. Slippy fell in behind him. The snow by now had piled belly-high on the horse and in two hours the pair progressed scarcely a mile, with the going harder every yard. Twice Slippy almost pitched into oblivion over the sheer cliffs; at last he turned back up the trail. Sounder followed him, for each was bound to the other now by ties as deep as life.

When hunger drove them forth from the lean-to again, it was up the mountain instead of down, for on the heights the snow was far less deep. In places the ridges were swept almost bare by the force of the wind. Up along the sparse spruce valleys they plodded, Slippy finding here and there some uncovered forage, and chewing many evergreen twigs for good measure. Sounder ran rabbits through the thickets.

Later that afternoon Slippy came upon a small herd of deer banded together in a winter "yard." Moved by an urge for companionship, he moved forward eagerly to join them, but the two leading bucks of the herd shook menacing heads.

Slippy was too forlorn and miserable to care what the deer thought of him. Even ill feeling was preferable to the empty loneliness of the peaks. He waited meekly, some fifty paces away, to see what would happen.

The snow round about was too deep for the deer to flee their yard, so the bucks contented themselves with stampings and repeated challenges. But Slippy had a disarming way of his own. He ruckled softly in his chest, and after an hour or so his quiet presence broke down resistance. The deer resumed their sketchy feeding, nibbling at the hanging branches of the trees and pawing down to the sparse feeding beneath the snow.

Later, when Sounder came in from a successful hunt, the deer were thrown into fresh panic. In fall or summer the deer would have fled like shadows and Sounder would have given chase in wild abandon. Now he came up meek and silent as Slippy himself and dropped panting beside his friend. Before long even his presence was accepted by the deer, for a magic truce had descended upon all.

By the time darkness came, horse and dog were learning the shelter and warmth that lies in snow when one is wise enough to burrow into it.

Each of the next four days they visited the ranch house, returning to the heights in the afternoon. Then on the fourth day they returned to find their wild friends had moved. The feeding had given out in the vicinity of the yard, and the deer had left to seek a better sanctuary.

Slippy followed along their trail, laboring slowly through the deep snow. He came upon the herd again a half mile away, tramping out a new yard which was to become a tragic prison for all of them. A thaw the next day was followed by another snowstorm. The high walls of the deer yard froze to the hardness of concrete, forming a prison from which there was no escape until another thaw.

Only Slippy's restlessness and his persistent urge to find his human friends saved him from sharing the fate of the deer. He was keeping vigil again at the ranch house when the freeze came. When he labored back to the deer yard he was unable to join his friends as usual. An iron crust had formed over the snow, and the pony stood nearly seven feet above the yard, looking dejectedly down on his imprisoned friends.

After four days, the feeding in the yard was consumed and the deer grew leaner and leaner, until the does and younglings were so weak they could hardly stand. Still no thaw came to liberate them.

The slow drama ended in tragedy one night when a mountain lion discovered the starving herd.

What followed was swifter and more merciful than starvation. Death came to them all, in their prison of ice.

Slippy, growing woodswise and wary, was warned of the menace that threatened on the lean dawn wind. A faint rank smell had come creeping into his consciousness, the musty reek of mountain lion. He knew it though he had never scented it before, and even to his peaceful intelligence that taint meant death. It sent him scrambling wildly out of the woods and onto a cleared slope just above.

Two days later Slippy and Sounder returned to find what was left of their friends, the deer. At the sight of the frozen and half-devoured carcasses, they did not wait for any chance encounter with the cougar. Keeping close together, they left that part of the mountain far behind and climbed toward the frozen peaks of the Divide. Now, because of the cougar, they avoided the dense timber for the rest of that day and therefore went hungry. And to add to their misery, another snowstorm started toward nightfall.

It was morning of the third day, with Sounder hunting far below, when Slippy rounded an outcrop of rock high above timber line and had the surprise of his life. A dozen or more fleecy hummocks of snow suddenly came to life about a hundred feet ahead of him.

Slippy was staring at his first band of mountain goats. One of them, the biggest, with pale fierce eyes, had a long, frosted white beard and black horns curling above his head. He snoofed explosively in challenge while the others melted away behind him.

The goats, fifteen of them, fled up over the rims as Slippy moved forward, but they could not go far because of the drifted snow. Slippy pressed on, disregarding the loud snoofing challenges of the old leader, who sought to engage Slippy in combat. But it takes two to make any sort of battle. Finding nothing to vent his wrath upon, the old Billy subsided at last into an occasional angry snorting and stamping.

When Sounder approached in search of his friend, the whole goat band disappeared like magic beyond a seemingly unscalable peak, and Slippy thought he had lost them for good. But next morning he found them again.

When the band moved, Slippy followed silently in their wake, edging closer by degrees. When they uncovered the short cured grass of the heights and ate, he also ate and found it good. The goats began to look upon him as a friendly, harmless creature. By the third day Slippy was suffered to feed and bed at will on the edge of the band during the daytime hours when Sounder was hunting afar. But the dog they would not accept.

At night old Sounder always found Slippy, and the two slept together in some cranny out of the wind. But by day Slippy continued to follow the goats. He found their feeding lean fare, but it kept life in his body.

In the second week the goat leader led the band along a series of narrow, precipitous ledges to the distant peaks. Slippy's small, trim hoofs were becoming almost as sure as those of the goats themselves. Acrobatic feats, however, were a bit beyond him. The narrow ledge the band had been following pinched sharply off into space. But ten feet below it a two-foot nubbin of rock protruded from the face of the cliff. The old goat leaped for it, balanced a moment, then dropped to another still farther on, and thence to another narrow ledge beyond. One by one the rest of the goats followed suit.

Slippy stood at the end of the ledge looking miserably after them. He could not follow, or even turn around. Misery seized upon him and he lifted his voice in a protesting neigh. The goats, however, paid no heed. Already they were out of sight.

There was but one thing to do. Cautiously, feeling for each foothold, Slippy began backing along the ledge down which he had come. There were four hundred yards of that before he reached a spot where he could turn. Up over the rims he went by a roundabout way, but the goats were nowhere in sight.

For ten days thereafter Slippy wandered the heights, miserably searching for his friends along all the streets and avenues of the high goat cities. And each day two bald eagles sailed close to him expectantly, waiting for some mischance to strike him down. But Slippy, with a surprising ruggedness and craft, was doing the unbelievable—meeting and beating the winter wild in its cruelest and grimmest aspect.

A fighting spirit had awakened in him, a spirit that harked back to his hardy ancestors. His clever brain, that had formerly contrived small tricks of mischief, now worked overtime for self-protection. He had profited by all the object lessons of the deer and goats, and added numerous observations of his own. The fierce

winds of the heights, he knew, could be depended upon to un-
cover enough herbage to keep life in his body, and at night he
kept from freezing to death by huddling close to Sounder on the
sheltered side of the peaks. But his civilized nature was dying the
seven deaths in those mountain solitudes, and many times a day
his lonesome whinny echoed among the crags.

Sounder too was doing the incredible, surpassing through necessity all normal bounds of his nature. Wolfish instincts came
uppermost in him, instructing him how to consume enough snow
for the water he needed, how to tell from afar when a deep snow-
bank held sleeping partridge, and how to dig out wood mice in
their deep runways when all other food failed. He grew lean and
gaunt as a specter, but somehow he survived.

A third week went by and January came, bringing with it a
still cold unlike anything Slippy had yet known. He still searched
the heights for his friends, and at length one afternoon he sighted
a number of white specks against a far-off cliff. A valley lay between, but Slippy, undaunted, descended clear to timber line,
bucked the deep drifts, and labored grimly up the other slope.
Before nightfall he had come up with the goat band again, whinnying his satisfaction.

January was a terrible month up on the roof of the world.
Storm after storm swept the heights. From the forested valleys
below the hunger call of wolves and coyotes sounded nightly,
and sometimes the whining scream of a cougar would split the
breeze. Even the wild goats began to feel the pinch of hunger, for
the snows were such that the highest peaks became mantled with
white.

Now came the time of greatest peril, when hunting in the
valleys grew lean and the mountain lions sought the peaks for
meat. The broad pads of these killers held them up on the deep
snow where the sharp hoofs of the goats cut through. The deadly
stalking of the great cats could not wholly be guarded against,

no matter what the craft of the goats. The cougars would prowl the heights until they found some point where the goats would have to pass. Lying in wait for hours until the band approached, the lion would drop like a bolt from some overhanging rock, and one of the band would pay with its life.

After each attack by a lion the goats would take refuge for days among the rim rocks. But they could not remain there indefinitely, and when hunger drove them down again the killers would again hang like a bad conscience to their trail. By the end of January five of the original fifteen goats had been killed, and still there was no break in the weather.

Slippy came through that grim month unscathed, partly because he was always struggling along at the tail end of the file of goats, and partly because the lions were suspicious of him, associating him and his scent with man, their greatest enemy. The old leader of the goats also escaped attack. That hoary patriarch would have welcomed facing a lion in fair combat. But the killers were cowards at heart, and had no stomach for tackling a four-hundred-pound fighting machine, with sinews of whalebone and a hide like a thick wool rug.

As February came and the deep snows still made hunting in the lower forests impossible for the cougars, the contest between the goats and the great cats came to an inevitable dramatic head. For weeks the goats had been growing warier and warier. They never approached a rock cliff without beating carefully up wind, eyes and nostrils alert for a sign of the enemy. For a fortnight there had been no casualties in the band, for they had lived on the leanest fare in order to avoid every possible ambush.

At last, on a still night when a dying moon bathed the white peaks in a spectral light, the lions, driven by unbearable hunger, brought the battle to the old patriarch.

Slippy and Sounder were some five hundred feet below the band this night. All were bedded near the brink of a broad, open ledge, where no enemy could possibly approach without first appearing boldly in the open. It was that hour before the dawn when night hunters that have found no kill turn desperate.

The jagged peaks roundabout leaned toward the morning stars, when an eddy of breeze carried the rank scent of lion to the sensitive nostrils of the old leading goat. He had the band on their feet in an instant. Then, after long minutes of tension, a mountain lion showed among the rocks of the distant cliff, another close behind. This was the pair that had ravaged the peaks all winter. Beyond all caution now, they advanced into the wash of moonlight, red-eyed with hunger.

The goats backed to the brink of the ledge, the old patriarch well to the fore, facing the cliff. Minutes of waiting passed. The lions flattened themselves to the snow, advancing but a few inches at a time, their eyes holding the goats with a murderous fixity. Never before had they carried the war into the open like this. Their every instinct was for waiting and indirection, but fiercer even than their blood lust was the gnaw of hunger. The big muscles of their shoulders bulged above their gaunt, crouched bodies.

Slippy, standing five hundred feet down slope, was trembling faintly, unable to make any other move. Weakened by cold and privation, he wanted only to sink down in the snow; wanted only to creep away and sleep. But the lions came on—so stealthily that they seemed not to move at all, save for their long tails that twitched like snakes. Puffs of icy wind sent sprays of snow across the ledge from the rocks above.

Even old Sounder seemed to have no battle challenge in him this night. For once he made no sound, but merely got to his feet, his hackles rising stiffly along his gaunt shoulders. As yet the lions had not seen him.

Abruptly the foremost lion launched himself forward in an attempt to pass the old leader's guard. But the bulky patriarch, agile as any kid, reared and whirled on his hind legs with a bawl of defiance, and a lightning thrust of his crinkly black horns caught the killer in mid-air. The lion was jerked to one side as if by invisible wires. Almost in the instant he alighted he returned to the attack, in a succession of short rushes and angry snarls. The *wheep-wheep* of his great mailed paws tore patches from the old goat's white coat but, wheeling and pivoting with flashing horns, the leader still managed to block the lion at every turn.

Back to the very brink of the ledge they maneuvered, till another step would have pitched them both into oblivion. Still by a miracle the cougar was unable to break through the guard to the huddled kids and nannies behind.

Then, into the breach, help came flying in a shaggy wolfish form. Old Sounder, who might have crept away unnoticed from that place of death and danger, had hesitated but a brief minute. Straight into the face of the cougar he launched his hundred and fifty pounds. What followed was a storm of tawny arms and legs and flying snow, amid a crescendo of screams and growls and the white flash of fang and claw.

The lion's mate, meanwhile, had been circling the rocks to come in from the opposite side and make a swift kill while the old patriarch was engaged. But no opening offered. Instead, there stood Slippy in her way, a chunky, sorrel-colored horse trembling in every limb but with white teeth bared, hoofs dancing, nostrils ruckling in a frenzy of defiance. Even as Sounder attacked, the lioness sprang from haunches like coiled springs. Slippy moved in the same instant. He pivoted and powerful hind legs shot out, catching the lioness a glancing blow on the shoulder.

With a fiendish squall the big cat struck the snow, then bounded to the pony's back, her four sets of claws sinking deep into his quivering sides. Slippy staggered, pitched to his nose but struggled up again, his wild whinnies of protest blending with the battle cry of the patriarch.

The mailed paw of the lioness crooked beneath Slippy's neck and wrenched cunningly. Her custom was to kill by dislocation.

Slippy bucked like a demon. His blunt teeth caught one silky ear of the attacker and ground it into a bleeding rag. The lioness screamed with rage and sprang free—unable, like all cats, to stand pain. She crouched for another spring, perilously close to the lip of the ledge, as Slippy wheeled with a desperate whinny. In that instant old Sounder was beside him. Somehow the dog had broken free of the lion and come to the aid of his friend.

Sounder sprang in with a roar; the lioness struck and sprang aside. Once more, terrible and avenging, Slippy swung around to deliver a broadside kick with his powerful hind legs. It landed squarely and soddenly against the big cat's ribs, flinging her back. She teetered a moment on the very brink, her claws rasping on the ice and snow, and Slippy kicked again. A moment the tawny body dangled over the snowy ledge, then slipped and pitched downward, writhing and screaming, into the gulf below.

The male lion, circling the old goat, turned his head at the death cry of his mate. It was only an instant, but for the patriarch, dancing on his hind legs preparing for a charge, it was enough. He drove in with a mighty thrust of lowered horns that rolled the killer over. Before he found his feet the old goat hit him again like a piledriver, while from the opposite side old Sounder was closing in to finish the kill.

It was too much for the lion. Before either opponent could reach him again, the killer of the peaks was streaking, belly down, for the shelter of the cliffs.

At that point Slippy and Sounder might have established themselves as masters of the mountain wilderness and all its inhabitants. To them it was an empty glory, however; particularly to old Sounder, wounded far more seriously than he knew. Torn and red and hardly recognizable, he collapsed presently on his side, his blood staining the snow. He gave but a few feeble thumps of his tail when Slippy came and stood above him.

It was two hours before his fevered wounds stopped bleeding.

All that day Slippy stayed close to his friend. The goat band, too, hovered near in a strange concern, drawn by the bond that had been established between them in battle.

That victory over the cougars seemed a winning over famine and the winter hardships as well, for at nightfall there came an abrupt break in the weather.

Before morning the snowy slopes were melting in a thousand tiny rivulets and through the silence sounded the occasional long, sucking *chug* of sinking snow. Mountain and forest seemed to relax and breathe again. There might come other freezes, but the worst of the winter was now over.

Meanwhile Sounder was fighting with the last supreme Enemy, and barely holding his own. Somehow Slippy seemed to know. By gentle nudges of the warm, inquiring nose, he kept rousing the old dog from his coma of pain and fever, urging him to follow down the mountain to the ranch house. Again and again through that long day the dog would rally and rise on shaky legs and follow Slippy for a hundred and fifty yards, only to sink down again and rest until strength was renewed.

Night had fallen when they reached the ranch. All was deserted still, but the corrals and pastures were almost free of snow, the warm breeze was like a benison, and the air was filled with the soft chuckle of trickling water. Stretched out on the ranch porch, Sounder let the old familiar scents and sounds slide through his ears and nose. His heart took strength and the shadowy Enemy faded away, defeated.

It was about noon next day, as the goat band fed slowly along the snowline above the ranch, that something startled them into sudden flight. Slippy saw them go and flung up his head, then wheeled at another movement and the old familiar sound of human voices.

Jesse Hunnicutt, with Jake Marden and young Jesse behind him, had just rounded a bend in the valley trail, each mounted and leading a pack animal. Releasing their pack horses at sight of Slippy, all three spurred forward with incredulous whoops and yells.

And Slippy? Flinging up his head with a wild whinny, he sprang from complete rest to full speed in a single shutter-click of time. Down the length of the great pasture he thundered to meet his friends, running with all that was in him, his small mountain-hardened legs moving like pistons in perfect rhythm. To the watching men his flying hoofs seemed never to strike the ground.

The riders reined in to gape, sitting their horses as though struck in stone. On he came, until he was eight feet in front of the horsemen. In the final instant before head-on collision, Slippy jerked aside with no slightest slackening of speed, then swept round and round them in great wild circles, whinnying again and again with happiness. The men continued to watch in silent fascination.

Always slimly built and lightly muscled, Slippy was now leaned down to the point of emaciation, the tendons like slender skeins at his wrists and hocks—but skeins of steel. He looked more than ever as if he might drift before the wind.

Jesse Hunnicutt was muttering as he watched. "Look at him, just look at him!" he cried. "There's an antelope and a greyhound rolled up in him—to say nothin' of a cannon ball! And that leg-work! And to think I left him for dead!"

They waited till Slippy had worked off some of his steam and joy and come to a stand. Then Jesse Hunnicutt dismounted, while young Jesse spurred toward the ranch house to look for his dog. The rancher was aware of a vague but definite shame as he approached the game little horse. He was guilty, as he saw it now, of rank desertion. Slippy's mane was a gnarled and matted mass from the winter winds; his lean sides were no longer sleek, but woolly as a range horse's—nature's desperate effort to help ward off the cold. The man's eye picked out the wounds along his back.

"Cougars, Boss!" cried Jake Marden. "The pore little cuss! I reckon he saw a thing or two besides cold and hunger up there among the peaks!"

"Well, I'll be John Brown!"

Jesse put a hand on Slippy's sturdy neck, then bent to run exploring, incredulous fingers over the solid chest and hocks and pasterns. He swore soulfully again. Never had he dreamed of seeing a two-year-old in such superb condition. In spite of cougars and cold, winter and hunger, or perhaps because of them, he was looking at a champion.

For a space man and horse stood gazing at each other across the great gulf of silence that hangs forever between the human and animal world. Had Slippy been human the gulf might never have been spanned after what had happened in the fall. But being animal, he bent his head to rub it lovingly against the man's sleeve. It was enough for him that the voices of his human friends once more fell blessedly on his ears.

Up at the ranch house old Sounder too had rubbed away that gulf as if it had never been, and young Jesse was kneeling on the porch step, his arms full of his old dog.

THE RUNAWAY

ROBERT FROST

Once when the snow of the year was beginning to fall,
We stopped by a mountain pasture to say, "Whose colt?"
A little Morgan had one forefoot on the wall,
The other curled at his breast. He dipped his head
And snorted at us. And then he had to bolt.
We heard the miniature thunder where he fled,
And we saw him, or thought we saw him, dim and gray,
Like a shadow against the curtain of falling flakes.
"I think the little fellow's afraid of the snow.
He isn't winter-broken. It isn't play
With the little fellow at all. He's running away.
I doubt if even his mother could tell him. 'Sakes,
It's only weather.' He'd think she didn't know!
Where is his mother? He can't be out alone."
And now he comes again with a clatter of stone,
And mounts the wall again with whited eyes
And all his tail that isn't hair up straight.
He shudders his coat as if to throw off flies.
"Whoever it is that leaves him out so late,
When other creatures have gone to stall and bin,
Ought to be told to come and take him in."

ANNA

Horse Star of "Aïda" Gets Final Cut

(*The New York Times,* March 23, 1940)

Anna, the aged white mare which in her long reign at the Metropolitan Opera House was as much a part of the regal splendor of Verdi's "Aïda" as the leading tenor and soprano, is dead. Anna died at the Pegasus Club, Rockleigh, N.J., last night of the infirmities of her advanced age of 39.

Anna's repertoire was confined only to "Aïda," but that was sufficient to give her lasting glory. Resplendent in her natural white coat, bedecked with glittering jewels, Anna's great moment was in the triumphal scene. In her long service—twenty-five years—Anna hauled many famous tenors onto the stage in this pièce de résistance of the Verdi work.

It wasn't much of a job, but it demanded a smooth disposition and an even temperament; Anna possessed these qualities. Many a horse in other operas of less volume had shied at the first outburst of the brasses. But Anna was different.

"She had talent," Earl Lewis, assistant general manager of the Metropolitan, said sadly when informed of Anna's death.

Came the triumphal scene and Anna was in all her glory. The brasses would reach a feverish crescendo and onto the stage would step Anna, hauling the chariot and the triumphant Rhadames.

Only once was Anna critical of the tenor, and that happened a score of years ago when the singer got off pitch. A couple of neighs from Anna and the tenor knew he was off key. In connection with

Anna's striking figure, Mr. Lewis recalled the story of a special patrolman who was stationed in the lobby of the Metropolitan.

This particular patrolman in his five years of service never had heard an opera. Came the night of "Aïda," with Caruso, Emmy Destinn and Pasquale Amato in the principal roles, and the house was jammed. Mr. Lewis persuaded the officer to come backstage and hear the triumphal scene. The audience roared its approval. Mr. Lewis turned to the officer and said: "How did you like it?"

There was a pause of several seconds, and the officer replied: "That's the swellest looking horse I've ever seen."

Anna saw service with Beniamino Gigli, Lauri-Volpi, Morgan Kingston, Giovanni Martinelli and Arthur Carron. She was active up to three years ago, when Douglas Hertz, owner of the Pegasus Club, purchased her and retired her to his club.

Anna had a motion-picture career. She carried Rudolph Valentino in "The Sheik" and Marion Davies in "When Knighthood was in Flower." Elisabeth Rethberg and Ezio Pinza, who often sang in "Aïda," lauded Anna's talents. Praising her ability never to miss her cue, they said she "knew her entrances and exits so well that the property man never had to worry."

ANNA DIES AT 39

Veteran Horse of Opera "Aïda"

(*New York Herald Tribune*, March 23, 1940)

Anna, the white horse which graced performances of "Aïda" at the Metropolitan Opera House many times, a contemporary of that stage of the late Enrico Caruso, died yesterday at the Pegasus Club, in Rockleigh, N.J., where she had lived in retirement for the last three years. She was born on August 26, 1900, and achieved an age almost as remarkable as her artistic career.

Besides appearing for many years in "Aïda," Anna had played in "Ben-Hur" and was with Rudolph Valentino in the "Sheik." She was also ridden by Marion Davies in "When Knighthood was in Flower."

She retired from the stage three years ago when Douglas Hertz, proprietor of the Pegasus Club, bought her and gave her the run of his pastures. "Even then," Mr. Hertz said, "at the age of thirty-six, Anna was one of the finest white mares I have ever seen."

On August 26, 1936, when Anna was thirty-six years old, Mr. Hertz gave a birthday party for her at the Pegasus Club, to which he invited fourteen horses and a mule. He had a birthday cake with candles and an abundance of carrots. Anna's charm and affability on this occasion won instant popularity and she received a lavender hat with a feather in it as the most glamorous horse of the party.

Her former associates at the Metropolitan were grieved by the news of her death.

"I was honestly grieved," said Elisabeth Rethberg, soprano, "to learn that Anna had passed away. She was a real trooper and in countless performances of 'Aïda' she carried off her part like a veteran. She never missed her cue and knew her entrances and exits so well that the property man never had to worry. She was a wonderful animal who lived to a ripe old age and earned her retirement."

Ezio Pinza, basso, was equally moved and expressed confidence that Anna had gone to "the Valhalla of horses."

"It is three years," he said, "since Anna last appeared in a performance of 'Aïda' in which I sang. There have been many times since in a performance of the opera when we all missed her tremendously. She was one of the finest looking animals I have ever seen."

Anna was a principal in one of the big moments of "Aïda"— the triumph scene. She bore Rhadames, the heroic leader of the Egyptian armies, when he returned after his victory over the Ethiopian troops.

FLIGHT
An Appreciation

JAMES C. BENDRODT

Lady, I wonder if on the day that you were born, you stood with your knees bent under you because of weakness, and I wonder if you trembled just a little as is the way of baby horses in their first few hours on earth. And yet I think I needn't wonder because I seem to know that this wasn't the way of things with you.

I know the kind of night that ruled your mother's world in the hours before you came among us. I can hear the shrill spring wind playing among the tall dry grass, and the only light your mother had to see by came from the pale cold stars that hung like lamps above her suffering head. And I know that when at last she dropped you that her world was hushed and quiet while she ministered to you where you lay stretched out on the hard brown earth. The sun, I think, was just below the dim horizon when you first struggled to stand upon your long slim legs, and I think you gained your feet that first time just as the sun burst over the rim of the world in all his golden glory, and there was only the call of a silver-throated bird to hail the advent of a champion.

And when the sun had risen I seemed to see you standing there —a baby horse, but straight and strong with your tiny head thrown up toward that lemon-tinted sky, and on your lips a shrill clear challenge to this strange cold world that you knew you'd conquer even then. I know you didn't tremble in that first short hour of life. I know you never did and never will.

Since these things happened, along with multitudes of other

people, I've seen you race so many times. I sometimes think that there has often been a faster race-horse. I know the pace you owned was quite superlative, but still I know that speed was not the quality that made you great. No, that was not the answer. You owned a queer sort of stark, remorseless courage that transcended mere speed as horsemen know it. I've seen you race so many times and on so many occasions I've seen you enter that last tumultuous furlong to all intents and purposes a beaten horse, and then I've watched you with the savage fighting spirit that was your hallmark defy the heartbreak of exhaustion, the screaming agony of outraged nerves and sinews, and go on and win. Yes, a million folk have seen you win your races just that way.

Well, lady, you have fulfilled your destiny, you who I trust will mother filly foals and colts to carry on the glamour of your name. You'll always have a stellar page among the annals of the great. But now what will they do for you? You brought a fortune to those who owned you. Along the triumphant path you trod you gave so many other things that men will always strive for. The joys and the thrills, the everlasting pride that comes to one who owns a horse as great as you were. Yes! What will they do for you? Well, they'll be kind to you. I'm sure of that. I like to think, indeed I feel I know, that when at last in some far paddock you lay your dauntless head down for the last time, and the stars hang like lamps in the sky above you, just as they did on the night when you were born, that it will be your old master's hand that soothes you, his easy voice that says that last good-bye.

THE SUBURBAN HORSE

H. C. BUNNER

I have often wondered where the suburban horse lives before he comes to the suburbs; and I have sometimes thought that there must be people who make a special business of going about all over the country and collecting misfit horses of odd, job-lot sizes and styles, for distribution in suburban towns.

City horses and real country horses may be readily divided into various grades and classes; recognizable even to one as ignorant of such matters as I am. Though every householder here—except myself—owns one horse, at least, I am sure that you could not pick anything remotely resembling a matched pair out of the whole lot. I am speaking, of course, of the true suburban horse. I have several neighbors of sporty proclivities, who own costly teams of high-blooded horses, which are spoken of in a reverential sort of way as "fine actors," or "grand steppers." I do not speak from personal knowledge of the quality of these animals; I only know that they walk as if they had corns, and that they are always sick; and these, I am assured, are signs of high blood and great commercial value in a horse. But I am not speaking about animals such as these. You may see their like everywhere where people are trying to get rid of their money. But the suburban horse belongs to the suburbs, and is a thing to be studied all by himself.

In the first place, he is no particular kind of horse—or he is any and every kind, as you please to put it. His quality, character and station among horses depend almost entirely upon his ownership and employment; and he has only to change hands to change his nature. He is one horse if *you* own him, and another horse if *I* own him; and he may be any number of horses in the course of his long and peaceful but much varied existence. Having no horse or carriage of my own, good or bad, to provide for, I am a mere spectator of other men's horses, and how they play their parts, and you have no idea how diversely they are presented unto me.

Take the case of Rix, for instance. I take his case because he is the horse I know best, and because he is one of the very few that I can recognize at sight. In the way of horse-flesh it takes something, as a rule, about as showy as a calico circus pony to attract my attention and fix itself in my memory. But Rix and I got personally acquainted when I first came to the town, and I have since watched his checkered career with a friendly interest.

When I first knew him he belonged to a market-gardener in the next county, who used to come to my door with his vegetables. The gardener was a very intelligent man, and I got into the habit of talking botany with him while I fed his own things to his own horse. The town was quite small then, and decidedly lonely at times, and even tree-peddlers and book-agents were welcomed with a cordiality and courtesy that sometimes lured them into thinking that we meant to buy. So I used to be very glad to see Rix and the market-gardener, and when the latter gave up the business because he said there was no profit in it, I really felt considerable remorse for the way I had pampered his animal with luxuries at his expense.

The gardener asked me if I knew anybody who wanted to buy a horse. I told him that I had heard the old butcher in Orchard Lane say something about buying a horse; and he asked me to speak to the butcher about it. This I did, and they met in my back yard, and the bargain was struck. I never saw my friend, the gardener, again; but when Rix came around with the butcher's meat, I felt as though he were quite an old acquaintance.

Now, up to this date, I wish you to observe, the horse was devoid of any noticeable characteristic. He had no pedigree. The gardener had bought him from a wandering Swede, and had named him Rix-Dollar, with a vague idea that he ought to do something Scandinavian in the matter. He was a very dark bay horse, neither large nor small, of an equable disposition, and quite sound and healthy. Indeed, I may say for Rix that he was never sick but once in his life. I was present when the butcher bought him, and I heard his points discussed; but I could not make out that they were different from those of any other horse.

In the course of a few months the old butcher died, and left no immediate successor. I had to go elsewhere for my meat; and I really missed the sight of Rix jogging deliberately on his daily rounds, with the white-bearded old butcher half-asleep in the wagon.

But one day we heard that a new butcher had taken the old place; and that the new butcher was a great sport, and was going to make things hum in the meat business in our town. I strolled around to Orchard Lane to see what the new butcher was like. He was not in his shop; but as I started homeward I heard a furious clatter of hoofs down the street, and, casting up my eyes, beheld a large, red-faced stranger in a showy vehicle of the dog-cart sort, driving a dark bay horse at a rattling clip. The man was the new butcher, and the horse was Rix—Rix in a showy harness with brass trimmings all over him, with bracelets on his ankles, and with a patent-leather shine on his hoofs. I marvelled much. The butcher did not interest me; but it was clear to my mind that either Rix was acting a part now, or that he had heretofore dissembled his true character. I didn't particularly object to his present frivolous worldliness, but I thought he ought to have let me know before that he was that kind of a horse.

Shortly after this, a friend of mine, whose knowledge of the noble Horse was so profound and pervasive that it came out in his clothes, spent a few days with me looking about the town, with a view to taking a house in the succeeding Fall. He happened to see the butcher drive by behind Rix, and he was as much impressed as a really horsey person ever allows himself to be. He told me that the dog-cart was entirely incorrect in the matter of style, and that the butcher didn't know how to drive; but that the horse was an uncommonly neat little animal, and that if he, my friend, had that horse for six months, he could make something of him.

"I've owned worse, myself, my boy, before this, I can tell you," he said, patting me encouragingly on the shoulder; and I felt that his praise of Rix reflected a certain glory on the whole township, including myself. I didn't say anything to him about Rix's earlier days; for I always make it a point to go light on such particulars when I am talking with a man who wears horse-shoe pins, and has gold whips and wheels and axle-trees, and other miniature imitations of stable upholstery on his watch-chain.

A few weeks later my friend wrote to me, asking me to see if I could buy Rix for him, and have him kept on a neighboring stock-farm until the Fall. He named the figure which he was willing to "go" for the horse. It was a figure that amazed me greatly, when I remembered the modest price for which he had been sold in my back yard. But I knew better than to say anything about this to my friend; for he was a very good friend, and I should have hated to lose him. Fortunately, it made no practical difference; for the sporty butcher had failed and fled from his creditors, and Rix was legally in the custody of the Sheriff, and bodily in a pasture lot adjoining my place, whence he occasionally wandered into my wife's flower-garden, and ate indiscriminately. Later in the season, a retired clergyman, with a family of five elderly daughters, came to board in my neighborhood, bringing letters of introduction to me. He was in search of a retired place in which to write a six-volume work on palæontology. After he had paid me six or eight protracted calls and set this fact forth at full length, I found him a retired place at a distance of about seven miles. He rewarded my kindness by hiring Rix from the Sheriff and driving his whole family into town three times a week.

In the Fall my friend, whom I shall call Mr. Fornand, came, and took a house in the town. He had to run out every day for a week or so, to get settled, and he frequently took his luncheon at my house. This was very pleasant for me, not only because my friend was good company, but because I stretched a point and told the palæontological clergyman that I had a gentleman who raced horses staying at my house, and he promptly stopped making visits to town. He stopped for so long, indeed, that I had almost forgotten him and Rix, too, when one day I came across his capacious carryall standing at the station. He told me that he was going away, and that the Sheriff was going to meet him there, and take charge of Rix again. Part of this was not pleasant news to me; and when, as I was hurrying homeward, I caught up with Fornand going in the same direction, and, shortly afterward, the Sheriff drove past us behind Rix, I said somewhat hastily to my friend:

"There, Fornand, there's that horse of the butcher's you wanted to buy in the Spring. I think you could get him now."

As soon as I had said this I knew that I had made a mistake. A Summer of palæontology had told on Rix, and he had absorbed something of the depressed and mildewed appearance of the prehistoric carryall behind him. But I confess I was somewhat startled when my friend burst out in wild guffaws of derisive mirth, and shouted:

"That horse the one I was looking at? Why, Great Scott! if that isn't the funniest thing I have heard in a year! That horse the butcher's? Well, Sage, I always knew you were pretty green about horses, but I *did* think you had enough gumption to know a first-class animal from an old plug like that."

I didn't attempt to argue with him; I was ashamed, anyway, of Rix's present appearance, and I thought I would let the matter drop. But it didn't drop. He guffawed all the way up to the house, and then he told my wife what a big joke he had on me. Afterward my wife said to me, kindly but pitifully:

"Well, my dear, I didn't think you knew much about horses; but I *should* have thought you would have known *Rix*."

For one moment I thought of setting myself right; and then I concluded to accept my humiliation as a deserved punishment. When a man carries Christian forbearance to the extent of making a plumb fool of himself, he ought to take the consequences.

Rix went at Sheriff's sale to the teamster who carted away my ashes, and to whom I advanced twenty dollars to buy him. He came to the house twice a week, but I hated to see him now, for he had become a neglected-looking, disreputable, shaggy-haired brute, with worn spots here and there on him, and a generally moth-eaten appearance. I was glad when the teamster sold him to the local expressman, although he was not a success in his new place. Having grown accustomed to hauling shamefully heavy loads, he suddenly found himself hitched, one fine Spring morning, shortly before Easter Sunday, to a light wagon, laden principally with paste-board boxes that had just arrived from New York. When he started to pull on this, he became intoxicated with his comparative freedom, and ran away down the street, scattering Easter millinery and dry-goods right and left. He was sent to the livery stable for safe-keeping; and there a tramp stable-boy, who had been a jockey, bought him for five dollars, took him in hand, treated him in the mysterious ways that are known to jockeys, and actually got him into such a condition that he sold him to an undertaker who had just started a shop in the town. The undertaker was a man who took pride in his business, and he fattened Rix up and groomed him and broke him to hearse so thoroughly that in a few months he was as sleek and wholesome-looking a horse as you would wish to see, and I felt proud of him whenever I met him. He attended only two or three funerals, but his dignity and style were much admired. When the undertaker gave up and went in search of an unhealthier town, there was lively competition for Rix at the auction of the business effects. He went to a local horse-dealer for one hundred and forty dollars. I attended the sale out of curiosity. As I was going away I met my friend Fornand, and I saw from his sheepish manner and from his vain endeavors to keep the catalogue which he held, out of my sight, that he had

BUCEPHALUS
A King's Horse

ALICE GALL AND FLEMING CREW

"Say no more, Orestes. My mind is made up. The horse Bucephalus shall be sold."

It was on a summer day, more than two thousand years ago, that these words were spoken by Philonicus, a wealthy man of Thessaly in Greece. The two men, Philonicus the master and Orestes his slave, stood under a plane tree at one end of a green field in which a number of horses were pasturing. Around this field stretched on all sides the wide flat plains of Thessaly. And far to the north rose the lofty peaks of Mount Olympus, believed in those days to be the home of mighty gods who ruled the world.

Both master and slave were dressed in the long flowing robes of their time. But the master's robe was richly embroidered in silver, as were the sandals on his feet. About his thick brown hair he wore a band of purple. Philonicus was a man accustomed to being obeyed, and when he had spoken these words to Orestes he turned away.

But the slave put out a hand as though to detain him. "Master," he said earnestly, "there is not in all Greece another horse like Bucephalus."

"Well do I know that, Orestes," Philonicus answered, "and his new master shall pay a princely sum for him. I mean to sell him to King Philip of Macedon."

"King Philip of Macedon!" the slave repeated in amazement.

"None other," replied Philonicus. "King Philip knows horses.

been among the unsuccessful bidders. I couldn't help it, and I didn't want to. I asked him what he wanted with that old plug. He reddened up; but he had too much capital invested in horsey jewelry to let me call him down.

"That horse is no plug," said he, "though he may have looked like one at one time. The man who's driving may be a plug, and that makes a horse look like a plug; but if you knew as much about a horse as I do, Sage, you'd know that in the hands of a right kind of man that would be the right kind of horse. And when your uncle tells you that, you don't want to forget it."

Consequently he hired Rix from his new owner, and put him into a scratch spike-team that he got up to impress a Bergen Point man who was thinking of buying his house. This occasioned Rix's one sickness. He caught pinkeye from a thoroughbred.

Since then Rix has been in several hands; but he is still recognizable to his old friends. He worked on a milk route for a while, which quite incapacitated him for the work of the homœopathic physician who bought him next, and who was dreadfully embarrassed by being drawn up in front of various houses where nothing on earth would have induced the inmates to call in an irregular practitioner.

He is now pulling the phaeton of an aged invalid lady, under the guidance of a groom in half-livery. From what I know of him, he is trying his best to assume the demeanor of quiet, slow-going and responsible respectability suitable to his present position. What changes of social status and personal appearance may be in store for him I cannot tell; for he is hardly more than fourteen years old, and, for a suburban horse, that is the prime of life.

His army rides into battle mounted on splendid chargers fit for the war-god Mars himself. And it is said that Philip of Macedon would rather lose six Generals than one good horse of war. He will find use of Bucephalus."

"Master," Orestes pleaded, "you would not send Bucephalus into the cruel wars of Macedon? You know well how gentle has been his training. Never has he felt the sting of the lash. Surely, my master, you will not sell Bucephalus to King Philip."

"Such is my plan," Philonicus answered shortly, and a look of greed came into his eyes as he added, "King Philip's wars have brought him much wealth. His treasury is full. I mean to make him pay handsomely for Bucephalus." And with this Philonicus walked away.

After his master had gone Orestes stood looking sadly off toward Olympus. If only some god would help him save Bucephalus, he thought. But the great mountain seemed very far away and he, Orestes, was a slave. He could expect little help from the gods.

Presently he whistled softly, a long clear note, and in a moment or two Bucephalus appeared at the edge of a grove of oak trees far across the field. Trotting over to where Orestes stood, the beautiful dark bay horse lowered his head so that the slave might stroke his nose and pull his silky ears. For a little while he stood so, scarcely moving at all, and then suddenly he thrust his muzzle forward, gave Orestes a playful shove, and was off down the field like the wind, his head held high, his tail streaming straight out behind him.

This was a favourite trick of his and Orestes always expected it. But today the slave could not laugh; his heart was too heavy. From the time Bucephalus was a tiny colt Orestes had looked after him, feeding him and caring for him each day, and brushing his coat to keep it sleek and shining. It was Orestes who had put a bridle on him for the first time and taught him to carry a man on his back.

Bucephalus had not liked this. The bit hurt his tender mouth and having a man on his back seemed a strange thing. But Orestes had been so kind and patient that soon the strangeness wore off, and Bucephalus no longer rebelled but gladly carried the slave, mile after mile, across the broad flat plains.

Thessaly is a fair land, and for Bucephalus life was pleasant. There was the wide green pasture with its soft grass and its grove of oak trees where the shade was welcome on hot afternoons. And there was a stream of cool water where he drank when he was thirsty and in whose quiet pools he stood, knee deep, when the flies and insects annoyed him.

What would the life of Bucephalus be after this Orestes wondered, as he watched the young horse galloping over the field? King Philip of Macedon was a powerful king, he knew, for the tales of his wars and conquests had spread over all that part of the world. It was said that even now he was planning greater wars, that he longed to rule over a mighty empire, and dreamed of a day when all Greece should be his.

And now because Philonicus was greedy for gold, and King Philip of Macedon was greedy for power, Bucephalus was to have a new master!

On a morning late that summer King Philip of Macedon and his son Alexander, a lad of sixteen years, were walking through the palace gardens. They were on their way to the parade grounds to inspect the soldiers at their morning drill. But they had gone only a little way when they were met by a guardsman who saluted and stood at attention.

"Have you a message?" King Philip asked.

"Yes, Sire," the guardsman answered. "A stranger from Thessaly would see you."

"What is his errand?"

"Sire, he would sell you a horse," the guardsman told him.

"A horse!" King Philip thundered. "And you come to me with such a thing! Do you take me for a stable boy? This is an affair for some petty groom. If the horse is sound, let him be bought."

"The horse is a good one, Sire," the guardsman replied, "but the price is very high and the officers who are charged with such matters feared your displeasure."

"We have gold to purchase what we need," the king told him sharply. "Go, tell my men to use their wits."

"The price the stranger asks is thirteen talents, Sire."

King Philip looked at the guardsman in amazement. "Thirteen talents!" he exclaimed. "Why, such a price would scarce be paid for twenty horses! Dismiss the man at once. Tell him King Philip is no fool."

The guardsman saluted again and turned to go, but the boy Alexander called to him. "Wait, Simonides," he said. "The stranger comes from Thessaly, did you say?"

"From Thessaly," replied the guardsman.

"It is a land of splendid horses," Alexander said. "Let us have a look at him, father. Who knows? He may excel all horses in your stables even as you excel all other men in Macedon."

King Philip looked down at his son and laughed. "Yours is a sound head, my son," he said, laying his hand on the boy's shoulder. "Your words are well spoken. We shall see this stranger and his horse."

"Have this man of Thessaly bring his horse to the west riding field," the king told the guardsman. "And have trainers from my stables there, to put the animal through its paces."

When King Philip and young Alexander reached the riding field they found a number of the king's trainers already awaiting them.

"Where is this stranger from Thessaly and his horse?" the king asked impatiently.

"The Thessalonian comes yonder, Sire," said one of the men pointing toward the stables, "but the horse is being fed a measure of oats by the Thessalonian's slave."

King Philip laughed aloud. "What say you to that, Alexander?" he exclaimed. "A king must stand waiting while a slave feeds a horse!"

The boy Alexander made no answer for just then the Thessalonian, accompanied by a guardsman, came and knelt before the king.

"Rise, man of Thessaly," King Philip bade him. "Your land of Greece, beyond Olympus, is not unknown to me. I have seen its beautiful cities, its splendid temples, and its wide, fertile plains. A fine land it is. But tell me," he broke off, "what of this horse who now eats his measure of oats in my stables? I would know about him, for if he be worth but half the price you ask he must still be a wondrous horse."

"You shall see for yourself, oh King," Philonicus replied. "He is a mount the gods might envy you. I am asking thirteen talents for him, but were he yours you would not part with him for many times that sum."

"Do you hear that, Alexander?" the king asked, turning to his son. "What think you of the Thessalonian's words?"

"Why think of them at all, father?" the boy replied. "The horse himself will speak a truer tale than many words. See! Here he comes!"

From the stables across the riding field came the horse with the slave Orestes on his back. Alexander grasped his father's arm excitedly and the two of them stood looking in admiration. "He is indeed a splendid creature," exclaimed the king at last.

Bucephalus was quivering with nervousness. These were strange surroundings to him. Strange voices were all about him and he had eaten his oats in a strange stable, with men he did not know staring at him. He would have been badly frightened now if Orestes had not spoken to him encouragingly and patted his back.

"Look, father," said Alexander. "Do you note the fine slender legs, the long body, and the narrow, well-shaped head?"

"Ay," his father answered, and then turning to Philonicus he said: "You shall have your thirteen talents, unless my trainers find some hidden flaw in him."

Two of the trainers stepped forward and grasped the bridle,

one on each side, while Orestes dismounted. He stood for a moment with his hand on the horse's neck. "A good friend you have been Bucephalus," he muttered. "May the gods send just punishment on any man who dares mistreat you!" Then with a quick look at the two trainers the slave went over and stood at his master's side.

"Get on his back and put him through his paces," the king ordered one of his trainers.

But this was easier said than done. For when the trainer made ready to mount, Bucephalus jerked his head angrily and strained at his bit. The strength of the two trainers was barely enough to hold him. Suddenly he reared straight up on his hind legs, almost pulling the two men off their feet.

"Easy, Bucephalus! Easy, good horse!" called Orestes, and leaving his master's side the slave hurried forward. "I will quiet him," he said to the trainers.

"Stay where you are, slave!" King Philip ordered sharply. "I must learn this horse's temper before I send him to my stables." Addressing his trainers he commanded that Bucephalus be mounted without further delay.

But King Philip's trainers, expert horsemen though they were, were not equal to this task. Bucephalus lunged and reared, kicking and biting at them if they so much as spoke to him. At last the king waved his hand in a gesture of disgust. "Take him away!" he cried angrily. "This horse is mad and altogether worthless. Turn him back to the slave. I would not give stable room to such a beast!"

The boy Alexander, who had watched these proceedings with flushed face and flashing eye, now stepped quickly forward. "Wait!" he called, and with a scornful look at the two trainers he said in a loud clear voice so that all might hear, "What an excellent horse they lose for want of address and boldness to manage him!"

King Philip turned sharply on his son. "Do you reproach those who are older than yourself," he said, "as if you knew more and were better able to manage the horse than they?"

Alexander answered boldly, "I could manage him better than the others do."

"And if you do not," said his father, "what will you forfeit for your rashness?"

Alexander did not hesitate. "I will pay," he answered, "the whole price of the horse."

In spite of his annoyance the king could not help laughing at the boy's bravado. And the company joined in the laugh.

But Alexander went swiftly to the horse's head, and motioning the trainers away he took the reins in his own hands. At once he turned Bucephalus about so that he was facing the sun, for he had noticed that the horse was shying nervously at his shadow on the ground. Then, stroking the sleek neck, Alexander talked to Bucephalus gently.

Little by little the horse grew quiet. There was something in the touch of the boy's hand, something in the sound of his voice that gave Bucephalus confidence. He knew that here was someone he could trust.

With a quick leap Alexander was on the horse's back. Bucephalus threw his head up sharply and quivered with surprise. But his fear was gone. He pawed the ground, eager to be running free over the plain with this boy on his back.

And now Alexander spoke a word of command. Instantly Bucephalus bounded away and the boy did not try to stop him. Giving him his head he urged him to even greater speed. The king and his company looked on aghast, fearing that at any moment Alexander might be thrown to his death. But Orestes the slave smiled. "The lad has fine judgment with horses," he said. "Bucephalus is in good hands."

At last the horse slackened his pace and Alexander, turning him about, came back to the riding field, his face beaming with triumph. King Philip of Macedon was more proud at this moment that he had ever been before. This boy of sixteen was destined to conquer. The gods were with him!

Scarcely waiting for Alexander to dismount he threw his arms about the boy's neck and kissed him. "My son," he cried, "look you out a kingdom equal to and worthy of yourself! Macedon is too small for you!"

Little did King Philip think at the time how soon these words would come true. Little did he dream that within four short years his son Alexander, mounted on this same Bucephalus, would ride out of Macedon at the head of a great army which was to conquer half the world.

Four short years—how quickly they passed. As the days went by Bucephalus grew to love the boy Alexander more and more. Eagerly he looked forward to those times when he could run, wild and free across the soft turf, the boy upon his back. This was what Bucephalus liked and it was what the boy liked. They understood each other, these two. They were friends.

But when the four short years were gone Alexander was no longer a carefree boy. He was a king. For King Philip was dead, leaving his dream of empire unfinished. His son Alexander must finish it for him. The young king's boyhood days were now over, he must turn to war and conquest. It was a hard task but he was ready.

One day there gathered on the parade ground a company of horsemen. They were no ordinary horsemen for they had shields and long sharp spears that glistened in the sunshine. These were fighting men.

A mighty cheer was lifted as young King Alexander approached mounted on his splendid horse Bucephalus. The fighting men lifted their spears in salute, and a moment later King Alexander and his army were on their way. Off they rode—to conquer a world.

Into far lands these Macedonians went. And always there was fighting and still more fighting. War! It was like a black cloud hiding the face of the sun. The world was turned into a world of hate and men forgot to be kind. There were years of hardship, suffering and bloodshed, but still Alexander's army marched on, conquering all before it.

King Philip's dream had come true, for Alexander was indeed the mightiest ruler in the world. His fame had reached into every land and wherever men talked of heroic deeds the names of the young king and his splendid horse were heard together. Alexander the Great and Bucephalus!

At first the horse had been frightened by the din of battle. The clang of weapons, the shouting of the soldiers, and the roaring and plunging of other horses round him had filled him with terror. But there was always the touch of his master's hand to quiet him, the sound of his master's voice to urge him on, and at last he grew accustomed to the tumult of war.

Through years of bitter fighting Bucephalus served his master well, carrying him triumphantly through battle after battle. And with each victory the ambition of King Alexander increased. With each new conquest that he made there came to him dreams of still greater conquest. He must go on and on, he told his men, until the whole world belonged to him.

But it takes a long time to conquer a world, and the life of a war horse is hard. There came a day when Bucephalus could no longer go into battle. He was growing old.

Alexander was forced to leave him in camp far behind the fighting lines. Here the faithful horse was well cared for and happy, and each day the king came and talked to him and Bucephalus would lower his head so that his master might stroke his nose and pull his silky ears. And sometimes he would thrust his muzzle forward and give King Alexander a playful shove, as he had once done with Orestes the slave in Thessaly.

Back in Thessaly the horse Bucephalus was not forgotten, and tales were told of the days when he was a colt and carried Orestes over the wide Thessalonian plains. The same flat plains still stretched away, and majestic Olympus, to the north, still raised its cloud-veiled summit. The years that had come and gone had brought little change to Thessaly.

"Orestes," said Philonicus one spring day, as again master and slave stood at the end of the green pasture, "do you remember the horse I sold for thirteen talents to King Philip of Macedon?"

"Yes, master," answered Orestes. "I shall not forget Bucephalus."

"Who would have dreamed," went on Philonicus, "that one day he would become the most famous horse in all the world? He is now almost as famous as the great Alexander himself."

"Bucephalus was always a good horse, master," Orestes said simply.

"Ay, a good horse," Philonicus repeated, turning away. "And thirteen talents was a good price, too. A handsome price, Orestes."

For a time the slave stood silent, and then walking slowly he went through the green pasture toward the little grove of trees. Midway of the field he paused and looked off at Mount Olympus. "A handsome price indeed," he said softly. "But if you had been mine, Bucephalus, not all the gold in Macedon could have bought you."

THE MALTESE CAT

RUDYARD KIPLING

They had good reason to be proud, and better reason to be afraid, all twelve of them; for, though they had fought their way, game by game, up the teams entered for the polo tournament, they were meeting the Archangels that afternoon in the final match; and the Archangels' men were playing with half-a-dozen ponies apiece. As the game was divided into six quarters of eight minutes each, that meant a fresh pony after every halt. The Skidars' team, even supposing there were no accidents, could only supply one pony for every other change; and two to one is heavy odds. Again, as Shiraz, the gray Syrian, pointed out, they were meeting the pink and pick of the polo-ponies of Upper India; ponies that had cost from a thousand rupees each, while they themselves were a cheap lot gathered, often from country carts, by their masters who belonged to a poor but honest native infantry regiment.

"Money means pace and weight," said Shiraz, rubbing his black silk nose dolefully along his neat-fitting boot, "and by the maxims of the game as I know it—"

"Ah, but we aren't playing the maxims," said the Maltese Cat. "We're playing the game, and we've the great advantage of knowing the game. Just think a stride, Shiraz. We've pulled up from bottom to second place in two weeks against all those fellows on the ground here; and that's because we play with our heads as well as with our feet."

"It makes me feel undersized and unhappy all the same," said Kittiwynk, a mouse-coloured mare with a red browband and the cleanest pair of legs that ever an aged pony owned. "They're twice our size, these others."

Kittiwynk looked at the gathering and sighed. The hard, dusty Umballa polo-ground was lined with thousands of soldiers, black and white, not counting hundreds and hundreds of carriages, and drags, and dog-carts, and ladies with brilliant-coloured parasols, and officers in uniform and out of it, and crowds of natives behind them; and orderlies on camels who had halted to watch the game, instead of carrying letters up and down the station, and native horse-dealers running about on thin-eared Biluchi mares, looking for a chance to sell a few first-class polo-ponies. Then there were the ponies of thirty teams that had entered for the Upper India Free-for-All Cup—nearly every pony of worth and dignity from Mhow to Peshawar, from Allahabad to Multan; prize ponies, Arabs, Syrian, Barb, country bred, Deccanee, Waziri, and Kabul ponies of every colour and shape and temper that you could imagine. Some of them were in mat-roofed stables close to the polo-ground, but most were under saddle while their masters, who had been defeated in the earlier games, trotted in and out and told each other exactly how the game should be played.

It was a glorious sight, and the come-and-go of the little quick hoofs, and the incessant salutations of ponies that had met before on other polo-grounds or race-courses, were enough to drive a four-footed thing wild.

But the Skidars' team were careful not to know their neighbours, though half the ponies on the ground were anxious to scrape acquaintance with the little fellows that had come from the North, and, so far, had swept the board.

"Let's see," said a soft, golden-coloured Arab, who had been playing very badly the day before, to the Maltese Cat, "didn't we meet in Abdul Rahman's stable in Bombay four seasons ago? I won the Paikpattan Cup next season, you may remember."

"Not me," said the Maltese Cat politely. "I was at Malta then, pulling a vegetable cart. I don't race. I play the game."

"O-oh!" said the Arab, cocking his tail and swaggering off.

"Keep yourselves to yourselves," said the Maltese Cat to his companions. "We don't want to rub noses with all those goose-rumped half-breeds of Upper India. When we've won this cup they'll give their shoes to know us."

"We shan't win the cup," said Shiraz. "How do you feel?"

"Stale as last night's feed when a musk-rat has run over it," said Polaris, a rather heavy-shouldered gray, and the rest of the team agreed with him.

"The sooner you forget that the better," said the Maltese Cat cheerfully. "They've finished tiffin in the big tent. We shall be wanted now. If your saddles are not comfy, kick. If your bits aren't easy, rear, and let the saises know whether your boots are tight."

Each pony had his sais, his groom, who lived and ate and slept with the pony, and had betted a great deal more than he could afford on the result of the game. There was no chance of anything going wrong, and, to make sure, each sais was shampooing the legs of his pony to the last minute. Behind the saises sat as many of the Skidars' regiment as had leave to attend that match—about half the native officers, and a hundred or two dark, black-bearded men with the regimental pipers nervously fingering the big be-ribboned bagpipes. The Skidars were what they called a Pioneer regiment; and the bagpipes made the national music of half the men. The native officers held bundles of polo-sticks, long cane-handled mallets, and as the grand-stand filled after lunch they arranged themselves by ones and twos at different points round the ground, so that if a stick were broken the player would not have far to ride for a new one. An impatient British cavalry band struck up "If you want to know the time, ask a p'leeceman!" and the two umpires in light dust-coats danced out on two little excited ponies. The four players of the Archangels' team followed, and the sight of their beautiful mounts made Shiraz groan again.

"Wait till we know," said the Maltese Cat. "Two of 'em are

playing in blinkers, and that means they can't see to get out of the way of their own side, or they may shy at the umpires' ponies. They've all got white web reins that are sure to stretch or slip!"

"And," said Kittiwynk, dancing to take the stiffness out of her, "they carry their whips in their hands instead of on their wrists. Hah!"

"True enough. No man can manage his stick and his reins, and his whip that way," said the Maltese Cat. "I've fallen over every square yard of the Malta ground, and I ought to know." He quivered his little flea-bitten withers just to show how satisfied he felt; but his heart was not so light. Ever since he had drifted into India on a troopship, taken, with an old rifle, as part payment for a racing debt, the Maltese Cat had played and preached polo to the Skidars' team on the Skidars' stony polo-ground. Now a polo-pony is like a poet. If he is born with a love for the game he can be made. The Maltese Cat knew that bamboos grew solely in order that polo-balls might be turned from their roots, that grain was given to ponies to keep them in hard condition, and that ponies were shod to prevent them slipping on a turn. But, besides all these things, he knew every trick and device of the finest game of the world, and for two seasons he had been teaching the others all he knew or guessed.

"Remember," he said for the hundredth time as the riders came up, "we must play together, and you must play with your heads. Whatever happens, follow the ball. Who goes out first?"

Kittiwynk, Shiraz, Polaris, and a short high little bay fellow with tremendous hocks and no withers worth speaking of (he was called Corks) were being girthed up, and the soldiers in the background stared with all their eyes.

"I want you men to keep quiet," said Lutyens, the captain of the team, "and especially not to blow your pipes."

"Not if we win, Captain Sahib?" asked a piper.

"If we win, you can do what you please," said Lutyens, with a smile, as he slipped the loop of his stick over his wrist, and wheeled to canter to his place. The Archangels' ponies were a little bit above themselves on account of the many-coloured crowd so close to the ground. Their riders were excellent players, but they were a team of crack players instead of a crack team; and that made all the difference in the world. They honestly meant to play together, but it is very hard for four men, each the best of the team he is picked from, to remember that in polo no brilliancy of hitting or riding makes up for playing alone. Their captain shouted his orders to them by name, and it is a curious thing that if you call his name aloud in public after an Englishman you make him hot and fretty. Lutyens said nothing to his men because it had all been said before. He pulled up Shiraz, for he was playing "back," to guard the goal. Powell on Polaris was half-back, and Macnamara and Hughes on Corks and Kittiwynk were forwards. The tough bamboo-root ball was put into the middle of the ground one hundred and fifty yards from the ends, and Hughes crossed sticks, heads-up, with the captain of the Archangels, who saw fit to play forward, and that is a place from which you cannot easily control the team. The little click as the cane-shafts met was heard all over the ground, and then Hughes made some sort of quick wrist-stroke that just dribbled the ball a few yards. Kittiwynk knew that stroke of old, and followed as a cat follows a mouse. While the captain of the Archangels was wrenching his pony round Hughes struck with all his strength, and next instant Kittiwynk was away, Corks following close behind her, their little feet pattering like rain-drops on glass.

"Pull out to the left," said Kittiwynk between her teeth, "it's coming our way, Corks!"

The back and half-back of the Archangels were tearing down on her just as she was within reach of the ball. Hughes leaned forward with a loose rein, and cut it away to the left almost under Kittiwynk's feet, and it hopped and skipped off to Corks, who saw that, if he were not quick, it would run beyond the boundaries. That long bouncing drive gave the Archangels time to wheel and send three men across the ground to head off Corks. Kittiwynk stayed where she was, for she knew the game. Corks was on the ball half a fraction of a second before the others came up, and Macnamara, with a backhanded stroke, sent it back cross the ground to Hughes, who saw the way clear to the Archangels' goal, and smacked the ball in before any one quite knew what had happened.

"That's luck," said Corks, as they changed ends. "A goal in three minutes for three hits and no riding to speak of."

"Don't know," said Polaris. "We've made 'em angry too soon. Shouldn't wonder if they try to rush us off our feet next time."

"Keep the ball hanging then," said Shiraz. "That wears out every pony that isn't used to it."

Next time there was no easy galloping across the ground. All the Archangels closed up as one man, but there they stayed, for Corks, Kittiwynk, and Polaris were somewhere on the top of the ball, marking time among the rattling sticks, while Shiraz circled about outside, waiting for a chance.

"We can do this all day," said Polaris, ramming his quarters into the side of another pony. "Where do you think you're shoving to?"

"I'll—I'll be driven in an ekka if I know," was the gasping reply, "and I'd give a week's feed to get my blinkers off. I can't see anything."

"The dust is rather bad. Whew! That was one for my off hock. Where's the ball, Corks?"

"Under my tail. At least a man's looking for it there. This is beautiful. They can't use their sticks, and it's driving 'em wild. Give old blinkers a push and he'll go over!"

"Here, don't touch me! I can't see. I'll—I'll back out, I think," said the pony in blinkers, who knew that if you can't see all round your head you cannot prop yourself against a shock.

Corks was watching the ball where it lay in the dust close to his near fore, with Macnamara's shortened stick tap-tapping it from time to time. Kittiwynk was edging her way out of the scrimmage, whisking her stump of a tail with nervous excitement.

"Ho! They've got it," she snorted. "Let me out!" and she galloped like a rifle-bullet just behind a tall lanky pony of the Archangels, whose rider was swinging up his stick for a stroke.

"Not to-day, thank you," said Hughes, as the blow slid off his raised stick, and Kittiwynk laid her shoulder to the tall pony's quarters, and shoved him aside just as Lutyens on Shiraz sent the ball where it had come from, and the tall pony went skating and slipping away to the left. Kittiwynk, seeing that Polaris had joined Corks in the chase for the ball up the ground, dropped into Polaris's place, and then time was called.

The Skidars' ponies wasted no time in kicking or fuming. They knew each minute's rest meant so much gain, and trotted off to the rails and their saises, who began to scrape and blanket and rub them at once.

"Whew!" said Corks, stiffening up to get all the tickle out of the big vulcanite scraper. "If we were playing pony for pony we'd bend those Archangels double in half an hour. But they'll bring out fresh ones and fresh ones, and fresh ones after that—you see."

"Who cares?" said Polaris. "We've drawn first blood. Is my hock swelling?"

"Looks puffy," said Corks. "You must have had rather a wipe. Don't let it stiffen. You'll be wanted again in half an hour."

"What's the game like?" said the Maltese Cat.

"Ground's like your shoe, except where they've put too much water on it," said Kittiwynk. "Then it's slippery. Don't play in the centre. There's a bog there. I don't know how their next four are going to behave, but we kept the ball hanging and made 'em lather for nothing. Who goes out? Two Arabs and a couple of countrybreds! That's bad. What a comfort it is to wash your mouth out!"

Kitty was talking with the neck of a leather-covered soda-water bottle between her teeth and trying to look over her withers at the same time. This gave her a very coquettish air.

"What's bad?" said Gray Dawn, giving to the girth and admiring his well-set shoulders.

"You Arabs can't gallop fast enough to keep yourselves warm —that's what Kitty means," said Polaris, limping to show that his hock needed attention. "Are you playing 'back,' Gray Dawn?"

"Looks like it," said Gray Dawn, as Lutyens swung himself up. Powell mounted the Rabbit, a plain bay countrybred much like Corks, but with mulish ears. Macnamara took Faiz Ullah, a handy short-backed little red Arab with a long tail, and Hughes mounted Benami, an old and sullen brown beast, who stood over in front more than a polo-pony should.

"Benami looks like business," said Shiraz. "How's your temper, Ben?" The old campaigner hobbled off without answering, and the Maltese Cat looked at the new Archangel ponies prancing about on the ground. They were four beautiful blacks, and they saddled big enough and strong enough to eat the Skidars' team and gallop away with the meal inside them.

"Blinkers again," said the Maltese Cat. "Good enough!"

"They're chargers—cavalry chargers!" said Kittiwynk indignantly. "They'll never see thirteen three again."

"They've all been fairly measured and they've all got their certificates," said the Maltese Cat, "or they wouldn't be here. We must take things as they come along, and keep our eyes on the ball."

The game began, but this time the Skidars were penned to their own end of the ground, and the watching ponies did not approve of that.

"Faiz Ullah is shirking as usual," said Polaris, with a scornful grunt.

"Faiz Ullah is eating whip," said Corks. They could hear the leather-thonged polo-quirt lacing the little fellow's well-rounded barrel. Then the Rabbit's shrill neigh came across the ground. "I can't do all the work," he cried.

"Play the game, don't talk," the Maltese Cat whickered; and all the ponies wriggled with excitement, and the soldiers and the grooms gripped the railings and shouted. A black pony with blinkers had singled out old Benami, and was interfering with him in every possible way. They could see Benami shaking his head up and down and flapping his underlip.

"There'll be a fall in a minute," said Polaris. "Benami is getting stuffy."

The game flickered up and down between goal-post and goal-post, and the black ponies were getting more confident as they felt they had the legs of the others. The ball was hit out of a little scrimmage, and Benami and the Rabbit followed it; Faiz Ullah was only too glad to be quiet for an instant.

The blinkered black pony came up like a hawk, with two of his own side behind him, and Benami's eye glittered as he raced. The question was which pony should make way for the other; each rider was perfectly willing to risk a fall in good cause. The black who had been driven nearly crazy by his blinkers trusted to his weight and his temper; but Benami knew how to apply his weight and how to keep his temper. They met, and there was a cloud of dust. The black was lying on his side with all the breath knocked out of his body. The Rabbit was a hundred yards up the ground with the ball, and Benami was sitting down. He had slid nearly ten yards, but he had had his revenge, and sat cracking his nostrils till the black pony rose.

"That's what you get for interfering. Do you want any more?" said Benami, and he plunged into the game. Nothing was done because Faiz Ullah would not gallop, though Macnamara beat him whenever he could spare a second. The fall of the black pony had impressed his companions tremendously, and so the Archangels could not profit by Faiz Ullah's bad behaviour.

But as the Maltese Cat said, when time was called and the four came back blowing and dripping, Faiz Ullah ought to have been kicked all round Umballa. If he did not behave better next time, the Maltese Cat promised to pull out his Arab tail by the root and eat it.

There was no time for talk, for the third four were ordered out.

The third quarter of a game is generally the hottest, for each side thinks that the others must be pumped; and most of the winning play in a game is made about that time.

Lutyens took over the Maltese Cat with a pat and a hug, for Lutyens valued him more than anything else in the world. Powell had Shikast, a little gray rat with no pedigree and no manners outside polo; Macnamara mounted Bamboo, the largest of the team, and Hughes took Who's Who, alias The Animal. He was supposed to have Australian blood in his veins, but he looked like a clothes-horse, and you could whack him on the legs with an iron crowbar without hurting him.

They went out to meet the very flower of the Archangels' team, and when Who's Who saw their elegantly booted legs and their beautiful satiny skins he grinned a grin through his light, well-worn bridle.

"My word!" said Who's Who. "We must give 'em a little football. Those gentlemen need a rubbing down."

"No biting," said the Maltese Cat warningly, for once or twice in his career Who's Who had been known to forget himself in that way.

"Who said anything about biting? I'm not playing tiddle-winks. I'm playing the game."

The Archangels came down like a wolf on the fold, for they were tired of football and they wanted polo. They got it more and more. Just after the game began, Lutyens hit a ball that was coming towards him rapidly, and it rose in the air, as a ball sometimes will, with the whirr of a frightened partridge. Shikast heard, but could not see it for the minute, though he looked everywhere and up into the air as the Maltese Cat had taught him. When he saw it ahead and overhead he went forward with Powell as fast as he could put foot to ground. It was then that Powell, a quiet and level-headed man as a rule, became inspired and played a stroke that sometimes comes off successfully on a quiet afternoon of long practice. He took his stick in both hands, and standing up in his stirrups, swiped at the ball in the air, Munipore fashion. There was one second of paralysed astonishment, and then all four sides of the ground went up in a yell of applause and delight as the ball flew true (you could see the amazed Archangels ducking in their saddles to get out of the line of flight, and looking at it with open mouths), and the regimental pipes of the Skidars squealed from the railings as long as the piper had breath.

Shikast heard the stroke; but he heard the head of the stick fly off at the same time. Nine hundred and ninety-nine ponies out of a thousand would have gone tearing on after the ball with a useless player pulling at their heads, but Powell knew him, and he knew Powell; and the instant he felt Powell's right leg shift a trifle on the saddle-flap he headed to the boundary, where a native officer was frantically waving a new stick. Before the shouts had ended Powell was armed again.

Once before in his life the Maltese Cat had heard that very same stroke played off his own back, and had profited by the confusion it made. This time he acted on experience, and leaving Bamboo to guard the goal in case of accidents, came through the others like a flash, head and tail low, Lutyens standing up to ease him—swept on and on before the other side knew what was the matter, and nearly pitched on his head between the Archangels' goal-posts as Lutyens tipped the ball in after a straight scurry of a hundred and fifty yards. If there was one thing more than another upon which the Maltese Cat prided himself it was on this quick, streaking kind of run half across the ground. He did not believe in taking balls round the field unless you were clearly overmatched. After this they gave the Archangels five minutes' football, and an expensive fast pony hates football because it rumples his temper.

Who's Who showed himself even better than Polaris in this game. He did not permit any wriggling away, but bored joyfully into the scrimmage as if he had his nose in a feed-box, and were looking for something nice. Little Shikast jumped on the ball the minute it got clear, and every time an Archangel pony followed it he found Shikast standing over it asking what was the matter.

"If we can live through this quarter," said the Maltese Cat, "I shan't care. Don't take it out of yourselves. Let them do the lathering."

So the ponies, as their riders explained afterwards, "shut up." The Archangels kept them tied fast in front of their goal, but it cost the Archangels' ponies all that was left of their tempers; and ponies began to kick, and men began to repeat compliments, and they chopped at the legs of Who's Who, and he set his teeth and stayed where he was, and the dust stood up like a tree over the scrimmage till that hot quarter ended.

They found the ponies very excited and confident when they went to their saises; and the Maltese Cat had to warn them that the worst of the game was coming.

"Now we are all going in for the second time," said he, "and they are trotting out fresh ponies. You'll think you can gallop, but you'll find you can't; and then you'll be sorry."

"But two goals to nothing is a halter-long lead," said Kittiwynk prancing.

"How long does it take to get a goal?" the Maltese Cat answered. "For pity sake, don't run away with the notion that the game is half-won just because we happen to be in luck now. They'll ride you into the grand-stand if they can; you must not give 'em a chance. Follow the ball."

"Football as usual?" said Polaris. "My hock's half as big as a nose-bag."

"Don't let them have a look at the ball if you can help it. Now leave me alone. I must get all the rest I can before the last quarter."

He hung down his head and let all his muscles go slack; Shikast, Bamboo, and Who's Who copying his example.

"Better not watch the game," he said. "We aren't playing, and we shall only take it out of ourselves if we grow anxious. Look at the ground and pretend it's fly-time."

They did their best, but it was hard advice to follow. The hoofs were drumming and the sticks were rattling all up and down the ground, and yells of applause from the English troops told that the Archangels were pressing the Skidars hard. The native soldiers behind the ponies groaned and grunted, and said things in undertones, and presently they heard a long-drawn shout and a clatter of hurrahs!

"One to the Archangels," said Shikast, without raising his head. "Time's nearly up. Oh, my sire and—dam!"

"Faiz Ullah," said the Maltese Cat, "if you don't play to the last nail in your shoes this time, I'll kick you on the ground before all the other ponies."

"I'll do my best when my time comes," said the little Arab sturdily.

The saises looked at each other gravely as they rubbed their ponies' legs. This was the first time when long purses began to tell, and everybody knew it. Kittiwynk and the others came back with the sweat dripping over their hoofs and their tails telling sad stories.

"They're better than we are," said Shiraz. "I knew how it would be."

"Shut your big head," said the Maltese Cat; "we've one goal to the good yet."

"Yes, but it's two Arabs and two countrybreds to play now," said Corks. "Faiz Ullah, remember!" He spoke in a biting voice.

As Lutyens mounted Gray Dawn he looked at his men, and they did not look pretty. They were covered with dust and sweat in streaks. Their yellow boots were almost black, their wrists were red and lumpy, and their eyes seemed two inches deep in their heads, but the expression in the eyes were satisfactory.

"Did you take anything at tiffin?" said Lutyens, and the team shook their heads. They were too dry to talk.

"All right. The Archangels did. They are worse pumped than we are."

"They've got the better ponies," said Powell. "I shan't be sorry when this business is over."

That fifth quarter was a sad one in every way. Faiz Ullah played like a little red demon; and the Rabbit seemed to be everywhere at once, and Benami rode straight at anything and everything that came in his way, while the umpires on their ponies wheeled like gulls outside the shifting game. But the Archangels had the better mounts—they had kept their racers till late in the game—and never allowed the Skidars to play football. They hit the ball up and down the width of the ground till Benami and the rest were outpaced. Then they went forward, and time and again Lutyens and Gray Dawn were just, and only just, able to send the ball away with a long splitting backhander. Gray Dawn forgot that he was an Arab; and turned from gray to blue as he galloped. Indeed, he forgot too well, for he did not keep his eyes on the ground as an Arab should, but stuck out his nose and scuttled for the dear honour of the game. They had watered the ground once or twice between the quarters, and a careless waterman had emptied the last of his skinful all in one place near the Skidars' goal. It was close to the end of play, and for the tenth time Gray Dawn was bolting after a ball when his near hind foot slipped on the greasy mud and he rolled over and over, pitching Lutyens just clear of the goal-post; and the triumphant Archangels made their goal. Then time was called—two goals all; but Lutyens had to be helped up, and Gray Dawn rose with his near hind leg strained somewhere.

"What's the damage?" said Powell, his arm round Lutyens.

"Collar-bone, of course," said Lutyens between his teeth. It was the third time he had broken it in two years, and it hurt him.

Powell and the others whistled. "Game's up," said Hughes.

"Hold on. We've five good minutes yet, and it isn't my right hand," said Lutyens. "We'll stick it out."

"I say," said the captain of the Archangels, trotting up. "Are you hurt, Lutyens? We'll wait if you care to put in a substitute. I wish—I mean—the fact is, you fellows deserve this game if any team does. Wish we could give you a man or some of our ponies—or something."

"You're awfully good, but we'll play to a finish, I think."

The captain of the Archangels stared for a little. "That's not half bad," he said, and went back to his own side, while Lutyens borrowed a scarf from one of his native officers and made a sling of it. Then an Archangel galloped up with a big bath-sponge and advised Lutyens to put it under his arm-pit to ease his shoulder, and between them they tied up his left arm scientifically, and one of the native officers leaped forward with four long glasses that fizzed and bubbled.

The team looked at Lutyens piteously, and he nodded. It was the last quarter, and nothing would matter after that. They drank out the dark golden drink, and wiped their moustaches, and things looked more hopeful.

The Maltese Cat had put his nose into the front of Lutyens' shirt, and was trying to say how sorry he was.

"He knows," said Lutyens, proudly. "The beggar knows. I've played him without a bridle before now—for fun."

"It's no fun now," said Powell. "But we haven't a decent substitute."

"No," said Lutyens. "It's the last quarter, and we've got to make our goal and win. I'll trust the Cat."

"If you fall this time you'll suffer a little," said Macnamara.

"I'll trust the Cat," said Lutyens.

"You hear that?" said the Maltese Cat proudly to the others.

"It's worth while playing polo for ten years to have that said of you. Now then, my sons, come along. We'll kick up a little bit, just to show the Archangels this team haven't suffered."

And, sure enough, as they went on to the ground the Maltese Cat, after satisfying himself that Lutyens was home in the saddle, kicked out three or four times, and Lutyens laughed. The reins were caught up anyhow in the tips of his strapped hand, and he never pretended to rely on them. He knew the Cat would answer to the least pressure of the leg, and by way of showing off—for his shoulder hurt him very much—he bent the little fellow in a close figure-of-eight in and out between the goal-posts. There was a roar from the native officers and men, who dearly loved a piece of dugabashi (horse-trick work), as they called it, and the pipes very quietly and scornfully droned out the first bars of a common bazaar-tune called "Freshly Fresh and Newly New," just as a warning to the other regiments that the Skidars were fit. All the natives laughed.

"And now," said the Cat, as they took their place, "remember that this is the last quarter, and follow the ball!"

"Don't need to be told," said Who's Who.

"Let me go on. All those people on all four sides will begin to crowd in—just as they did at Malta. You'll hear people calling out, and moving forward and being pushed back, and that is going to make the Archangel ponies very unhappy. But if a ball is struck to the boundary, you go after it, and let the people get out of your way. I went over the pole of a four-in-hand once, and picked a game out of the dust by it. Back me up when I run, and follow the ball."

There was a sort of an all-round sound of sympathy and wonder as the last quarter opened, and then there began exactly what the Maltese Cat had foreseen. People crowded in close to the boundaries, and the Archangels' ponies kept looking sideways at the narrowing space. If you know how a man feels to be cramped at tennis—not because he wants to run out of the court, but because he likes to know that he can at a pinch—you will guess how ponies must feel when they are playing in a box of human beings.

"I'll bend some of those men if I can get away," said Who's Who, as he rocketed behind the ball; and Bamboo nodded without speaking. They were playing the last ounce in them, and the Maltese Cat had left the goal undefended to join them. Lutyens gave him every order that he could to bring him back, but this was the first time in his career that the little wise gray had ever played polo on his own responsibility, and he was going to make the most of it.

"What are you doing here?" said Hughes, as the Cat crossed in front of him and rode off an Archangel.

"The Cat's in charge—mind the goal!" shouted Lutyens, and bowing forward hit the ball full, and followed on, forcing the Archangels towards their own goal.

"No football," said the Cat. "Keep the ball by the boundaries and cramp 'em. Play open order and drive 'em to the boundaries."

Across and across the ground in big diagonals flew the ball, and whenever it came to a flying rush and a stroke close to the boundaries the Archangel ponies moved stiffly. They did not care to go headlong at a wall of men and carriages, though if the ground had been open they could have turned on a sixpence.

"Wriggle her up the sides," said the Cat. "Keep her close to the crowd. They hate the carriages. Shikast, keep her up this side."

Shikast with Powell lay left and right behind the uneasy scuffle of an open scrimmage, and every time the ball was hit away Shikast galloped on it at such an angle that Powell was forced to hit it towards the boundary; and when the crowd had been driven away from that side, Lutyens would send the ball over to the other, and Shikast would slide desperately after it till his friends came down to help. It was billiards, and no football, this time—billiards in a corner pocket; and the cues were not well chalked.

"If they get us out in the middle of the ground they'll walk away from us. Dribble her along the sides," cried the Cat.

So they dribbled all along the boundary, where a pony could

not come on their right-hand side; and the Archangels were furious, and the umpires had to neglect the game to shout at the people to get back, and several blundering mounted policemen tried to restore order, all close to the scrimmage, and the nerves of the Archangels' ponies stretched and broke like cobwebs.

Five or six times an Archangel hit the ball up into the middle of the ground, and each time the watchful Shikast gave Powell his chance to send it back, and after each return, when the dust had settled, men could see that the Skidars had gained a few yards.

Every now and again there were shouts of "Side! Off side!" from the spectators; but the teams were too busy to care, and the umpires had all they could do to keep their maddened ponies clear of the scuffle.

At last Lutyens missed a short easy stroke, and the Skidars had to fly back helter-skelter to protect their own goal, Shikast leading. Powell stopped the ball with a backhander when it was not fifty yards from the goal-posts, and Shikast spun round with a wrench that nearly hoisted Powell out of his saddle.

"Now's our last chance," said the Cat, wheeling like a cockchafer on a pin. "We've got to ride it out. Come along."

Lutyens felt the little chap take a deep breath, and, as it were, crouch under his rider. The ball was hopping towards the right-hand boundary, an Archangel riding for it with both spurs and a whip, but neither spur nor whip would make his pony stretch himself as he neared the crowd. The Maltese Cat glided under his very nose, picking up his hind legs sharp, for there was not a foot to spare between his quarters and the other pony's bit. It was as neat an exhibition as fancy figure-skating. Lutyens hit with all the strength he had left, but the stick slipped a little in his hand, and the ball flew off to the left instead of keeping close to the boundary. Who's Who was far across the ground, thinking hard as he galloped. He repeated, stride for stride, the Cat's manoeuvres with another Archangel pony, nipping the ball away from under his bridle, and clearing his opponent by half a fraction of an inch, for

Who's Who was clumsy behind. Then he drove away towards the right as the Maltese Cat came up from the left; and Bamboo held a middle course exactly between them. The three were making a sort of Government-broad-arrow-shaped attack; and there was only the Archangels' back to guard the goal; but immediately behind them were three Archangels racing all they knew, and mixed up with them was Powell, sending Shikast along on what he felt was their last hope. It takes a very good man to stand up to the rush of seven crazy ponies in the last quarters of a cup game, when men are riding with their necks for sale, and the ponies are delirious. The Archangels' back missed his stroke, and pulled aside just in time to let the rush go by. Bamboo and Who's Who shortened stride to give the Maltese Cat room, and Lutyens got the goal with a clean, smooth, smacking stroke that was heard all over the field. But there was no stopping the ponies. They poured through the goal-posts in one mixed mob, winners and losers together, for the pace had been terrific. The Maltese Cat knew by experience what would happen, and, to save Lutyens, turned to the right with one last effort that strained a back-sinew beyond hope of repair. As he did so he heard the right-hand goal-post crack as a pony cannoned into it—crack, splinter, and fall like a mast. It had been sawed three parts through in case of accidents, but it upset the pony nevertheless, and he blundered into another, who blundered into the left-hand post, and then there was confusion and dust and wood. Bamboo was lying on the ground, seeing stars; an Archangel pony rolled beside him, breathless and angry; Shikast had sat down dog-fashion to avoid falling over the others, and was sliding along on his little bobtail in a cloud of dust; and Powell was sitting on the ground, hammering with his stick and trying to cheer. All the others were shouting at the top of what was left of their voices, and the men who had been spilt were shouting too. As soon as the people saw no one was hurt, ten thousand native and English shouted and clapped and yelled, and before any one could stop them the pipers of the Skidars broke on to the ground, with all the native officers and men behind them, and marched up and down, playing a wild northern tune called "Zakhme Bagan," and through the insolent blaring of the pipes and the high-pitched native yells you could hear the Archangels band hammering, 'For they are all jolly good fellows,' and then reproachfully to the losing team, "Ooh, Kafoozalum! Kafoozalum! Kafoozalum!"

Besides all these things and many more, there was a Commander-in-Chief, and an Inspector-General of Cavalry, and the principal veterinary officer in all India, standing on the top of a regimental coach, yelling like schoolboys; and brigadiers and colonels and commissioners, and hundreds of pretty ladies joined the chorus. But the Maltese Cat stood with his head down, wondering how many legs were left to him; and Lutyens watched the men and ponies pick themselves out of the wreck of the two goal-posts, and he patted the Cat very tenderly.

"I say," said the captain of the Archangels, spitting a pebble out of his mouth, "will you take three thousand for that pony—as he stands?"

"No, thank you. I've an idea he's saved my life," said Lutyens, getting off and lying down at full length. Both teams were on the ground too, waving their boots in the air, and coughing and drawing deep breaths, as the saises ran up to take away the ponies, and an officious water-carrier sprinkled the players with dirty water till they sat up.

"My Aunt!" said Powell, rubbing his back and looking at the stumps of the goal-posts, "that was a game!"

They played it over again, every stroke of it, that night at the big dinner, when the Free-for-All Cup was filled and passed down the table, and emptied and filled again, and everybody made most eloquent speeches. About two in the morning, when there might have been some singing, a wise little, plain little, gray little head looked in through the open door.

"Hurrah! Bring him in," said the Archangels; and his sais, who was very happy indeed, patted the Maltese Cat on the flank, and he limped into the blaze of light and the glittering uniforms, looking for Lutyens. He was used to messes, and men's bedrooms, and places where ponies are not usually encouraged, and in his youth had jumped on and off a mess-table for a bet. So he behaved himself very politely, and ate bread dipped in salt, and was petted all round the table, moving gingerly; and they drank his health, because he had done more to win the Cup than any man or horse on the ground.

That was glory and honour enough for the rest of his days, and the Maltese Cat did not complain much when his veterinary surgeon said that he would be no good for polo any more. When Lutyens married, his wife did not allow him to play, so he was forced to be an umpire; and his pony on these occasions was a flea-bitten gray with a neat polo-tail, lame all round, but desperately quick on his feet, and, as everybody knew, Past Pluperfect Prestissimo Player of the Game.